*A
Harlequin
Romance*

OTHER
Harlequin Romances
by MARY WIBBERLEY

1717—BLACK NIALL
1739—BELOVED ENEMY

MASTER
OF SARAMANCA

by

MARY WIBBERLEY

HARLEQUIN BOOKS   TORONTO
WINNIPEG

Original hard cover edition published in 1973
by Mills & Boon Limited.

© Mary Wibberley 1973

SBN 373-01775-8

Harlequin edition published April 1974

Printed in Canada

1775

CHAPTER ONE

THE first time Jane saw the man, he was Making a Scene. No gentleman, and certainly no lady, she thought wryly, would ever Make a Scene. She bit her lip and quickly looked down to the open magazine on her knee, trying to shut out the noise of raised voices in the baking hot airport. Aunt Dorothy was thousands of miles away in England, yet her precepts – invariably spoken in capital letters – lingered. Jane could almost feel the disapproving presence at her shoulder as she tried to ignore the shouting, gesticulating crowd by the desk in the large white-walled shed that served as main airport building on this, the last stage of her journey to Saramanca Island.

It was no use. It was as impossible to ignore it as it would have been to ignore Aunt Dorothy in full flow. Reluctantly Jane's head went up and she looked again at the man causing the row. He was taller than everyone else, towering over the small knot of officials, and the bowed Chinese woman clutching her shabby cardboard case, and several interested onlookers who had presumably nothing better to do than watch. The man was furious, that much was clear. Yet his voice was not raised. When he spoke, it was forcefully – and the others listened briefly before setting off again, arms waving, brows being smitten in apparent despair. Jane had no idea what it was all about. The Chinese woman, old and grey, was impassive and oddly dignified in the midst of all the turmoil.

'Looks like we'll be here till they've gotten it sorted out.' She looked up quickly at the man hovering beside her, clearly American, camera slung round his neck over a dazzling flowered shirt.

'Yes. I don't know what it's about, though.' Jane smiled shyly at the man, in his forties, very tanned, with springy ginger hair and laughing brown eyes. He sat down beside her, clearly taking her reply as an invitation to talk. Aunt Dorothy wouldn't approve of this either, Jane thought. Come to think of it, there wasn't much she did approve of, except Aunt Dorothy.

'Seems to me the big fellow,' he nodded at the man who was now leaning over the desk and writing hastily while three white-uniformed officials argued quietly among themselves, 'is objecting to the Chinese woman going on the plane to Saramanca – leastways, that's the impression I get.'

Jane looked across the room at him. What chance did that poor woman stand against a man like that? None, apparently. Even now the crowd was dispersing. One of the officials was leading the old woman away, leaving her to carry her own case.

'Oh, the beast!' She wasn't aware she'd spoken aloud until the man beside her grimaced.

'Well, he looks like a man who gets his own way, I reckon.' He passed Jane a card. 'Let me introduce myself. Jackson T. Miller.'

She read the bold black script on the business card, and in one corner an address in New York, and nodded her thanks and made as if to hand the card back. He waved her away, and peered at her overnight bag. 'Keep it, honey. You're going to Saramanca?'

'Yes. For a – a holiday.' Jane hesitated over the last word. She couldn't tell this stranger her reasons. She couldn't talk about her journey to anyone – yet.

Jackson Miller stood up. 'I'll get us a drink. What's yours?' Jane hesitated, then seeing his open friendly expression, swallowed the doubts, and said shyly: 'Oh, just something cool, please. And my name's Jane. Jane Ritchie.'

'Pleased to meet you, Jane.' Jackson grinned and stuck out his hand. 'Not every day I get the chance to talk to a pretty girl. Stay there, I'll be right back.' He vanished in the crowd, now moving about normally, all excitement over. The incident might never have been. The big man had vanished, but something lingered. Jane felt a small shiver run through her. She had only seen him at a distance, but even from there she'd received the impression of ruthless strength emanating from him. Very dark, and tanned, he had been dressed in a fawn bush suit, casually elegant, that had emphasized his powerful frame. She wouldn't see him again, that was something to be thankful for. And there were worse people than this friendly American to be travelling with on the last leg of a long tiring journey. Something of the depression that had settled over Jane before she'd left London so many hours before began to lift. She wasn't doing the wrong thing at all. Everything would turn out all right, in spite of Aunt Dorothy's doom-laden prophecies.

Jane looked ahead, but she saw nothing of the people, nor did she hear the shrill chatter of many different tongues. For a few seconds she was back in London, reliving that last bitter encounter with her aunt . . .

'It's your last chance. If you go, I won't have you back here – ever!' Aunt Dorothy was standing by the window, her back to Jane. As she turned slowly round, two pink spots blazing high on her cheeks, Jane felt a pang almost of pity sweep through her. Suddenly she saw her aunt as she really was, a lonely, embittered middle-aged woman who was having to face the fact that for the first time in her life, her niece was defying her.

7

'Aunt Dorothy,' Jane's voice was low, but she managed to keep it steady, 'I know you've been very kind letting me live here for the last six years. I appreciate all you've done for me – but can't you understand, I want to see my father again? Can't you try and see my point of view just for a minute?'

'He didn't want to see you when he walked out on your mother twelve years ago. You were six. What do you remember, eh? Tell me that. Nothing. He was no good then, never was, never will be.' Aunt Dorothy's hands were clutching the back of the armchair. Her knuckles showed white with tension, and the colour had gone from her face.

Jane shook her head. 'No. He has written – lots of times. But I would never have known, would I? If I hadn't bumped into the new postman that day and he asked me if I'd let him have those beautiful stamps for his son, if I didn't want them – I'd never have found out. No wonder you always got to the letter box first in the morning—'

'I did it for your own good.' The old woman's voice was shrill. 'I didn't want you upset—'

'They were mine. You h-had no right to keep them from me—'

'I had every right. You've lived under *my* roof, taking my charity—'

Jane held the last precious letter very tightly. Somehow it gave her courage. She was no longer afraid of the woman who had dominated her life since the age of twelve, since her mother had died. 'I – I didn't realize how much you r-resented h-having me. I'm sorry, but I'll do my best to r-repay you, when I'm at teacher training college, I'll take a job at weekends—' She stopped at the sight of her aunt's angry, twisted, grim face. Tears rushed to her eyes. It was a shock to discover suddenly that her

8

aunt had begrudged looking after her all this time – and yet was it? Had there not been clues – had she not, in a way, realized all along, but tried to ignore it? And now Jane had made her choice, and there was no backing out. Come what may, she would go to see her father. He wasn't well enough to travel, or he would have come to England. He had told her this in the letters, the letters that had been kept locked in a box in her aunt's desk, unopened. Jane had read them all, twelve of them, two a year, from different places all over the world – all except the last four, which were from an island in the Indian Ocean, a place called Saramanca. The stamps were beautiful, with pictures of exotic birds and flowers. Stamps that had caught the eye of the new young postman and caused her aunt's shameful secret to be revealed. Jane had written immediately to the address on the back of the flimsy airmail envelope, and back had come a cable five days later, a brief message that was to change her entire life. She knew it by heart. 'Letter following with air fare. Please come. Your loving Father.'

Swallowing the tears, Jane turned and picked up her cases. There was nothing more to be said . . .

'Hey, wake up, Jane, honey. This ice is melting.'

She blinked, brought back abruptly to the present, to see her new friend grinning broadly as he watched her.

'I'm sorry, I was miles away.' She took the proffered glass, thanked the American, and drank gratefully of its cool green depths.

Jackson slid beside her. 'Another fifteen minutes and we'll be off.'

Jane fought back the sensation of panic that assailed her. They were so near now . . . What if Aunt Dorothy had been right – was she being reckless and foolhardy? The thoughts whirled madly round. Three more hours and they would be there. Suddenly she wanted very much to know about this island where her father lived.

'Have you been to Saramanca before?' she asked the American as he lifted his glass. He surveyed her thoughtfully across the frosted rim, his eyes alert yet reminiscent.

'Yep, once, during the war. Never forgot it. That's why I'm going back.'

'And what's it like? Please tell me.' Jane found herself holding the glass tightly as if something important were about to happen.

He laughed. 'It'll be different now, I guess, but it's a big place, say sixty miles long – looks something like a giant fish from the air – very green, lush vegetation – a rich-looking place,' his eyes had a faraway look, as if he were already stepping off the plane. 'Yes, ma'am, sure is something. Miles of sugar cane growing there. Remember to look when we're going in to land.'

'And you're going for a holiday?'

'Yep, a trip into the past, you might say.' He stopped and gave her a sudden grin. 'Hey, never mind me. What's a little girl like you doing travelling all the way from England on your own?' And there was such kind concern on his face that Jane found herself telling him very briefly about hearing from her father, and his surprising invitation. Somehow she knew that this man wouldn't think her absurd or foolish. 'And,' she finished, 'now I'm nearly there, I'm feeling terribly nervous.' She smiled at him, his face intent as he listened. He gave a low whistle and shook his head.

'Jane, honey, that's marvellous! You've not seen him for twelve years? It'll be some reunion, I'll bet.' He patted her arm. 'Just hand me back my card a moment, will you?'

Puzzled, Jane did so, and he wrote something on the back, then handed her the card again. 'I've written the name and phone number of my hotel down. Do me a favour, will you? Ring me after you're settled in. I'd enjoy a call from you.' Jane put the card back in her bag.

'All right, I will. Thanks.'

The metallic, almost indistinguishable voice of an announcer came over the tannoy. 'Will passengers for Saramanca please make their way to the main door.'

'That's us.' Jackson stood up and gallantly offered his hand to assist Jane. Minutes later they were walking across baking concrete to where their plane waited, its wings glittering in the relentless glare from the sun. Heat shimmered, making the ground appear to shift and move, and everything had an unreal quality. About ten others were making their way out with them to where a smart grey-uniformed air hostess waited at the top of the steps leading up to the plane. She greeted them all with a broad welcoming smile and ushered them inside the comparatively cool aircraft, the smallest Jane had been on since the start of her journey. Butterflies of apprehension fluttered wildly inside her. This was it.

Sitting at the window seat looking back to the small crowd in the doorway, watching them off, Jane experienced a feeling of relief that there was no sign of the tall stranger. Several planes had left since the unpleasant scene inside the airport building. Presumably he had gone on one of them. There had been no sign of the Chinese woman either. Jane wondered what had happened to her. The last sight of the old woman being led away was something that would stay with her for a long time, she knew. As she was about to turn away from the window to speak to her companion, busily studying papers from his briefcase, she stopped and gasped in dismay. 'Oh, no!'

'What is it?'

'Look.' Jane pointed to where a tall figure was saunter-
ing out from the building. It was the man himself, the big
man who'd caused the trouble, now walking towards the
plane – and looking as if he had every intention of board-
ing it. He had taken his jacket off, and was carrying it
over his shoulder, one finger hooked in the loop, looking
splendidly arrogant and indifferent to everything.

'Oh, him,' Jackson seemed only mildly interested. 'I
thought he'd gone.'

'So did I,' answered Jane grimly. 'How big did you say
Saramanca was?'

'Big enough not to have to bump into him, if that's
what you mean,' he chuckled. 'Say, you really don't like
him, do you?'

'No.' She turned wide eyes to the friendly man beside
her. 'I don't like anyone who uses their money, or
influence, or whatever, to bully those weaker than themselves.'

Jackson shook his head slowly. 'It's one of the hard
lessons you have to learn in life, honey. It happens all the
time, and there ain't nothin' anyone can do about it – and
you sure look mad at this moment. Your eyes have an
angry sparkle – say, you know you're really pretty! You
remind me of my youngest daughter – did I tell you I've
got three? I've a photo somewhere—' he patted his jacket
pocket and fetched out a bulging wallet. 'There you are.
Vikki's on the right, see,' he pointed a stubby finger at one
of three suntanned leggy girls in shorts smiling whitely at
the camera. There was pride in his voice as he spoke of
them, and of his wife who hated flying, but was following
on by boat, and would arrive in a week. Jane was glad of
the opportunity to have something to look at besides the
formidable man who was just getting on the plane, duck-

12

ing his head, coming down the aisle towards them . . .

'They're all very good-looking,' she told him sincerely, trying hard to ignore the fact that the air hostess was fluttering round the man who had just settled himself in a seat at the rear of the plane. There was a whispered consultation that she couldn't hear, and the hostess vanished towards the pilot's cabin. Gone to tell him we can leave, thought Jane angrily, now that the V.I.P.'s on board at last.

She forced herself to concentrate on the half dozen snaps being presented for her approval, making appropriate remarks as Jackson passed each one to her. She knew what he meant about the likeness to his daughter. The girl was tall, possibly a little more than Jane herself, who was five foot seven in her bare feet. Her hair was long and straight and dark too, and there was a faint resemblance about the girl's eyes, large, thickly lashed. Jane handed the photos back with a smile. She was in spite of everything, very conscious of the man sitting at the back. As the warning came to fasten seat belts she obeyed automatically. So he was going to Saramanca. And Jackson had said it was a large island. Perhaps, after they had left the airport there, that would be the last they would see of him. Anyway, she thought, I shall be seeing my father again after all this time. Nothing was quite as important as that . . .

The heat struck them as they left the plane. Jane stumbled on the staircase, and was glad of Jackson's steadying hand on her arm. He looked at her, eyes alight with curiosity, and a kind of shared happiness. 'Your pop be here to meet you, Jane?'

She shook her head, blinking a little in the intensely bright sunlight. 'No. He's asked a neighbour to meet me. I sent him a photo in my last letter. He said she'll find me. Oh, I'm feeling a little sick!'

'I know, honey, I know. Say, I'll wait until this friend comes, just in case.'

'You're very kind, but I'll be—'

'Think nothin' of it. Think I'd abandon you now? Besides, what if *he* speaks to you?'

'You mean that man?' Jane pulled a face. 'I doubt it.'

They were at the bottom of the steps now, and following the air hostess tripping her neat way across dazzling white concrete to the airport building, one long low Nissen hut boldly emblazoned with:

'Saramanca International Airport Welcomes You.' Jane took a deep unsteady breath of the hot heavy air. She was really here, at last. And soon she would be reunited with the father she had last seen so many years ago. The father who had written again and again – but she had never known, perhaps would never have known if it hadn't been for a young postman's idle question . . .

'I'm sorry. What did you say?' Jackson's voice jerked her back to the present.

'That little lady looks as if she's waving to you,' he repeated. Jane looked towards the small crowd clustered behind a wooden barrier. Hankies were being waved, happy voices shrilled, and she saw the small fair-haired woman right at the end, dressed simply in a flowered dress. She was holding up a photograph, and it seemed as if her eyes held Jane's as she smiled.

'Yes, I think you're right.' The slight sense of unreality left Jane. She knew that this was the right woman. It wasn't a dream at all. He father *was* really here, he had sent for her . . .

Minutes later, the brief Customs formalities over, they

were walking to meet the woman, who came towards them, a delighted smile on her features. Jane was instantly drawn to her, for she wore an air of warmth and kindness, like some invisible cloak.

'My dear, I knew it was you right away. I'm Megan Davis, your father's next-door neighbour, you might say. Did you have a good journey?' Blonde hair casually tied back in a silk scarf of deep blue, she was probably in her forties, with a pleasant face, and blue eyes that sparkled with warmth and laughter.

'Lovely, thanks – but I'm rather tired,' confessed Jane. She introduced Jackson, who was hovering politely a few feet away, to Megan, and the two shook hands.

'Can we give you a lift anywhere, Mr. Miller?' Megan inquired.

'No, thanks, ma'am. I should have a hire car waiting some place. It's been a pleasure meeting you, Mrs. Davis. I just wanted to make sure someone turned up for Jane. You don't forget to call me now, you hear?'

'I hear,' Jane laughed. 'Thank you for looking after me.'

They watched him walk away to a row of cars, and Megan smiled. 'He looked very pleasant. Now, Jane, before we go, do you want to freshen up?'

Minutes later they were on their way. Jane's luggage was stowed neatly in the boot of the smart red sports car Megan drove. As they left the airstrip, an odd thing happened. Megan tooted the horn and waved, and Jane looked round, thinking it was Jackson. But it was a white Mercedes that flashed past them, and as it did, the driver saluted Megan in return. It was none other than the big man, the troublemaker!

'I didn't know he was coming back on your plane!' Megan turned a surprised face to Jane, then, seeing her expression, added: 'Why, Jane, what is it?'

Jane shook her head. 'Nothing.' Then, feeling that it might seem rude, she explained: 'I – we saw him at Gaver Airport. He was having an awful row with–' she hesitated, '–some officials.'

Megan began to laugh. 'Heavens! No wonder you looked so startled. That's Gavin Grant all over.' Her slender hands were skilful on the wheel as they drove along the wide straight road through lush green palms and exotic bushes with brightly coloured flowers that lined their way. 'What was it all about?'

'I never really found out,' Jane answered quietly, aware that she was on tricky ground. This man – this Gavin Grant – was apparently a friend of Megan's. She must not say what she really thought, and yet she could not lie. 'Jackson seemed to think he was trying to stop a Chinese woman from getting on our plane. She stood there holding this huge cardboard case – and they took her away. We didn't see her again.' In spite of her efforts to be quite impartial, something of her feelings must have come through, for Megan gave her an odd look, then smiled.

'I'm sure it wasn't what it seemed.'

'No. How is my father?' Jane asked. She didn't want to talk about that man Gavin any more.

'Not very well, Jane. But he's so looking forward to meeting you again, you know. He's been like a child for the past few weeks, ever since you said you were coming. Mac had to sedate him more than once.'

'Mac?'

'Doctor Duncan Macdonald. Known to everyone on the island as Mac. He's never lost his Scots accent – you could cut it with a knife! He looks after your father. They're old friends as well, and will gossip for hours if you let them.'

'What – what is the matter with my father?'

Megan didn't look at Jane. She was busy concentrating on avoiding a pony and trap whose driver seemed to think the middle of the road was the only place to be.

'We don't know. Mac wants him to go and see a specialist friend of his in Ceylon, but he won't hear of it. Perhaps, now you're here, you might be able to persuade him.'

Jane had a curious fluttering sensation inside her. 'I'll try,' she answered quietly. 'Of course.'

'Good.' Megan patted her arm. 'I'm glad you're here, Jane. It'll be lovely having a woman to talk to, you know. I seem to be surrounded by men!'

Jane laughed. 'Is that bad?'

Megan's laugh echoed her own. 'Well, no, but you can't talk the same to them, can you? My son Colin will probably try and whisk you away, but I'm going to be firm.'

'Colin? How old is he?' Jane imagined a teenager.

'Twenty-three. He works for Gavin, of course. But you don't know anything about us, I keep forgetting! Oh dear, you must remind me if ever I go on and you don't know what I'm talking about.'

Jane shook her head. 'I don't know anything about anybody yet, but I'm dying to learn.'

'I'm sure you are. Well, I live near your father. When I say next-door neighbour, it's true in a sense, but our houses are perhaps half a mile away from each other. I've been a widow for seven years and live with Colin. Then your father has his home, where he lives alone except for Ellen, his housekeeper, who's an absolute sweety – but very bossy! Then there's Gavin—' she stopped at Jane's involuntary gasp. 'What have I said?'

'You mean he – Gavin – is a neighbour too?'

'Why yes! My dear, you should see *his* place! You undoubtedly will, of course. It's fabulous. But then he practically owns the island – that's why I was so surprised to see him. He flies his own plane, a Cessna, usually. Still, he's a law unto himself, as you'll find out soon enough.' She chuckled. 'Then there's Leonie Smythe and her daughter Sara – but they're a few miles away. You'll meet them too – I'd be interested to know what you think of them.'

Something in the way she said it made Jane glance quickly at her, to meet a look of bland innocence.

'They're friends of yours?' she asked tentatively.

'I'd hate to prejudice you, my pet, so 'nuff said. Suffice to say that they're very keen to meet *you* – seeing you'll be staying very near to Gavin.'

'You mean—' Jane hesitated, not sure of what the older woman meant, but with some slow, unbelievable idea forming.

'I mean, my dear, that Leonie is very anxious for her dear daughter to have as little competition as possible.'

'Then she's no need to worry – if you mean what I think you mean,' said Jane, with a faint smile.

'You obviously haven't looked in any mirrors lately,' Megan's sweet smile caught Jane's eye. 'Has no one ever told you what a beautiful girl you are?'

Jane felt the painful warm tide rush up to her face. 'Y-you don't need to try and make me feel—' she began, agonized.

'My dear girl, perish the thought! You really don't know, do you!' Megan really did have an attractive voice, low and warm. 'Your photo didn't do you justice at all. If *I* had those lovely dark green eyes, I'd be quite happy, I can tell you!'

Jane was silent. She suddenly realized that Megan

spoke sincerely, and it gave her a warm glow inside. Aunt Dorothy had drilled it into her so constantly that she was a 'Plain Jane' that she had accepted it, as she had accepted everything her aunt said, without argument. It made life a little easier that way. Now she was gradually being made aware that perhaps Aunt Dorothy was not a paragon of virtue, whose every opinion was absolutely and unarguably right, as Jane had come to believe in the past six years.

There was the beginning of civilization now. Pleasant villas could be glimpsed through thick palm trees; white low buildings with painted shutters, seen in a blur as the car whizzed past. Jane exclaimed: 'It's so lovely. I didn't realize—'

'We're coming to Gavin's place now. Look to your left, Jane. There – can you see?'

Distantly shimmering in the heat, Jane caught sight of a tall house with green shutters and red pantiled roof, surrounded by a garden full of trees and lush rich flowers of every imaginable colour and variety.

'Yes, I can. That's where he lives?' And as she asked this they passed the gates, lacy black wrought iron, gilt-tipped, flung wide open, with a red gravel drive winding away into the distance.

'That's where he lives. And he gives parties – wow!' Megan shook her head. 'Jane, you wouldn't believe them. They're the talk of Saramanca.'

'Oh, yes, I would, thought Jane silently. Her head throbbed with the heat and a sudden surge of dislike for the man that Megan, quite clearly, rated highly. He was a bully, the worst sort – one with money and power. She was determined not to go to one of his parties – even in the unlikely event of him inviting her.

And then excitement of a different sort filled her as she

realized with fast beating heart that they must be nearing her father's house. What would it be like? Clearly there was wealth here. And what was it Aunt Dorothy had said? 'He'll probably be living in a grass-roofed hut on some beach.' If she were here now! Jane clasped her hands tightly together, willing herself to calmness.

'Thank you for meeting me, Megan,' she said. 'It was very kind of you.'

Megan laughed. 'Not at all. It was the very least I could do for your father. He's been a good neighbour to Colin and me these past three years. Besides, I must confess I was curious to see what you looked like. I only hope I'm there when you meet Leonie and dear Sara.'

'Oh, dear – I hope so too!' confessed Jane.

'We're here.' And they turned into a wide curved drive, very similar to Gavin Grant's. But there was less distance between the road and the low white villa which now greeted them. Jane gasped in astonishment and pleasure as the house appeared, her eyes taking it all in; the long verandah with slender white pillars supporting the green pantiled roof; bright green shutters flung open to let the sun in, and all around them the sight and scent of verbena, roses, mimosa growing rampant round the lush lawns.

'Oh, Megan, I didn't know – I never imagined—' she began, then stopped. Megan regarded Jane thoughtfully as she brought the car to a halt before the rich teak door with its wrought iron bolts and knocker.

'You know, I don't think you did,' she said slowly, then shrugging. 'Well, come on, my dear. Your father's waiting for you.'

Something puzzled Jane about the way she had spoken – but it wasn't until later that she discovered why. Now, tiredly, she got out from the car. Heat enveloped them

20

instantly, moist, intense, that brought beads of perspiration to Jane's face in seconds. Megan came round to take her arm and saw the look on her face. 'You'll get used to it,' she said. 'And the air conditioning in the car was working perfectly for once – it's very temperamental – you'll have to remember to conserve your energy in the afternoons. It gets much cooler and pleasanter in the evenings, I assure you.'

Together they went up the steps and Megan pushed open the door, which was ajar. They were in a cool white-walled hall, with thin rugs on the dark wood polished floor. Numerous pictures hung on the walls, and a guitar, the rich dark wood contrasting beautifully with the stark white behind it. Jane gasped with delight on seeing it, and was about to speak when a voice came:

'Megan? Is that you? Have you brought my daughter?'

'Here, John,' Megan sang out. 'We're coming.'

They entered a large sitting room to the right. It had at the back wide french windows looking out over more gardens that sloped down towards a forest of glossy-leaved, softly waving palms. Cool cane furniture was dotted about the room, which had an air of ordered elegance with more pictures filling the walls. But it was the man who held Jane's attention. All else faded as he rose from the settee with extended arms.

'Jane, my daughter. My Jane!' His voice was husky with emotion, and as if in a dream, she went towards him. This was the man she had dreamed about, and never imagined to see again. He was taller, thinner, and older than her memory allowed, and yet John Ritchie was a handsome man, his dark hair, faintly grey-streaked, brushed back from a broad lined brow, his eyes, so like his daughter's gentle and pain-filled. There was a kindness about him that enveloped her as she went into his arms. 'Oh, Daddy,' she gasped tearfully. 'Daddy!'

'Jane, my child! After all these years.' Silently, wordlessly, they clung to each other. Then John Ritchie held her at arm's length.

'Let me see you. I still can't believe it! You're really my daughter!'

'I'm really your daughter!' Jane was half laughing, half crying. 'I've so much to tell you – about why I never wrote—'

'No. Not now – not yet. That can wait. You told me enough in your letters, Jane. You don't need to tell me what Dorothy's like. Where's Megan?'

Jane looked round, having forgotten the other woman in the excitement of reunion. Her father went on: 'Gone to coax some long drinks out of Ellen, I should imagine. Well, sit down, child. Tell me about your journey.'

Sitting beside him on the settee, Jane told him of the long plane journeys, the stops, and the growing heat at each airport. She was telling him about the American when Megan came in carrying a tray.

'Ellen allowed me to bring this in myself,' Megan told them with a smile. 'She'll be in with some cakes in a moment.'

As they sipped delicious iced coffee, she added: 'We saw Gavin at the airport. I didn't know he was coming in on Jane's plane.'

John Ritchie raised his eyebrows. 'Nor I. Strange he didn't mention it. He was here only yesterday.' He looked at Jane. 'Well, and what did you think of him, eh?'

Before Jane could think of an answer Megan laughingly interrupted: 'I'm afraid Jane's had an unfortunate first impression of him, John. There was a scene at Gaver airport – and he apparently was the cause of it!'

John Ritchie smiled and exchanged a look of shared understanding with Megan. 'Ah, I see! He can be pretty formidable when he's in one of his tempers. Well, never mind. She'll see he's not such an ogre when we introduce them, I'm sure. Now tell me, Jane, what do you think about Saramanca? Is it like you imagined?'

With a sigh of relief, Jane answered. She was rapidly tiring of the way 'that man' – as she had begun to think of him – cropped up in every conversation; she didn't want to talk about him, or even think about him, but it would be difficult if others insisted on dragging his name in every few minutes. She told them truthfully of her surprise at seeing the beautiful villas on the island, the splendour of the place itself, especially in contrast to the bleakness of the tiny, baking hot airport.

Ellen, a huge coloured woman, came in on slippered feet, carrying a large plate of cakes and sandwiches. She was introduced by Jane's father, who obviously held her in affectionate regard. When she had gone there was a pause, then Megan looked at her watch.

'Well, I must go now. Colin's taking me to the Murrays tonight. They're giving a party for Shirley.' She turned to Jane. 'Some more friends on the other side of the island. You could have gone too, but I'm sure you want an early night after all that travelling.'

'Yes,' Jane smiled her thanks. 'And thank you once again for meeting me.'

'Think nothing of it.' Megan leaned over and kissed John's cheek. ' 'Bye. I'll pop in tomorrow to see you both. 'Bye, Jane. I'll see myself out. I know you two have a lot to talk over.'

She went quietly out, and Jane's father sighed. 'Ah, Megan's a good friend. You'll like her son Colin too. Oh, Jane, this is going to be a good holiday for you – I'll try

23

my best to make it so.'

'It's enough to be here,' Jane whispered, tears pricking at the back of her eyes. 'I never realized — I never thought—'

'No,' John Ritchie's hand covered hers for a moment. 'No regrets for what is past. That's finished and done. The future's all we need to think about now. I know you've only just come – but I want you to think seriously about staying, making your home here.'

His words had a strange effect on Jane. It was as if she had been expecting them all along, had known he would say them.

'I – I—' she began.

'Ssh, not now. I don't want you to say anything yet. Just leave it. I'm a wealthy man, Jane. I've been lucky in some ways – and I have no one to share it with, except you. But the decision is yours, and I'm not going to rush you, never fear that.' He smiled at her. 'I feel ten years younger just seeing you. You're so like your mother—' he paused, then went on more slowly: 'And I have a lot to tell you – to explain – but not now. There's time enough when you're rested from your travels. Now,' this more briskly, 'I'll get Ellen to show you your room. She's been getting it ready for days, so for heaven's sake praise it.' He leaned over to press a bell on the wall.

Jane smiled tiredly, then remembering something, said: 'There was a guitar in the hall. Do you play it?'

His eyes lit up. 'I used to. Don't tell me you do?'

'Yes, I learned it at school. I love to play. I wanted to bring mine, but couldn't because of the baggage allowance.'

Her father laughed. 'That's marvellous! My little Jane plays the guitar! I can't believe it. You know, it was the first, the only instrument I ever learned to play. Promise you'll give me a tune tomorrow?'

'I promise, Father.' Jane leaned over to kiss him as Ellen came in, her slippers flap-flapping on the shiny floor.

'You'll be wantin' to sleep awhile,' she said. 'An' your room's ready, honey. Come on with me.'

Jane followed the woman upstairs, remembering her father's injunction to praise the room. His words were unnecessary. Her gasp of surprised delight would have been sufficient to tell the housekeeper that her efforts had not been wasted. The bedroom was a large sunny room at the front of the house. Even with the cool grey blinds drawn down at the two windows, the light was sufficient to see the measured spaciousness of the whitewood fittings, and the large luxurious bed of white wrought iron, with pink lacy spread.

'Why, Ellen, this is beautiful!' sighed Jane. She went to touch the vase of pink hibiscus on the gleaming dressing table. As she turned, it was to surprise a look almost of sadness on the coloured woman's face. Ellen smiled, and it was gone.

'I'm goin' down now. Bathroom's next door. Sleep well. You'll do your dad a power of good.' With these words she left the room, and Jane heard her slippers clipping down the stairs. Five minutes later she was fast asleep.

When Jane woke it was dark, and the room was cool. Suddenly hungry, she got out of bed, slipped on fluffy mules and housecoat, and went to the bathroom. She could see a light from downstairs, and after a moment's hesitation, went quietly down. If Ellen was still up, she hoped to get something to eat. Quietly down the hall she went, and the dim light shone on the guitar, and the paintings ... Jane stopped before one, her hunger forgotten as she gazed at the bright colours of the picture of a fisherman by his boat. It was in oils, and in the dimness became more exciting, and mysterious. A faint spark of memory flickered and stirred ... it was almost as if Jane had seen it before. Yet how could she have?

Puzzled, she went quietly on, drawn by the warm glow of a lamp from a room at the end of the corridor, then she pushed open the door at the end, and she was in the kitchen.

Ellen stirred in her rocking chair, her eyes opened, and giving Jane a broad smile, she said: 'You're hungry, ain't you?'

'Yes. I just woke up. Ellen. I'm sorry if I disturbed you.'

'Not me, child. I was jus' restin' mah eyes, honey. I knew you'd wake about now. They all do after the journey.' She padded to the refrigerator standing in the corner. 'Sit you down. There's some cold chicken. It'll fry nicely with rice, and won't take but a few minutes.'

'Oh, but the chicken on its own will be lovely.' Jane's stomach protested strongly at the very thought of having to wait, and Ellen's remarks about 'they all do', implying hordes of visitors, slid unnoticed into the back of her mind. She looked round now, dark eyes gleaming. 'You'll eat properly here.'

Jane sat down. There was a finality in the other's tone that brooked no argument, and she remembered Megan's words about Ellen.

'Thank you, Ellen,' she said obediently. As she watched the housekeeper's deft hands preparing the food, she said: 'I saw a painting in the hall just now. Did my father bring a lot of pictures with him when he came here?'

Ellen's startled glance left the stove. 'Why, bless you, child, they're all his. I mean, he painted them.

Didn't you know?'

Her astonishment was only matched by Jane's own. 'You mean – my – my father's an artist?' It was incredible.

'He surely is. Just about the most famous one Ah can remember. Why, he sells 'em all over the world. You really didn't know?'

Numbly Jane shook her head There was so much she didn't know, could never have imagined. Yet now things were beginning to fall into some sort of pattern. Megan's look when she'd exclaimed at the beauty of the house, and now Ellen's surprise. Almost as if they had *expected* her to know of her father's fame. She bit her lip, suddenly shy and unsure of herself. What must they all think of her?

'I've known nothing of my father, nothing at all, Ellen, until I found out about his letters, and replied.' She looked up at the woman, a kind of desperate appeal in her eyes, and Ellen's face softened at the sight of Jane's fresh young beauty, her hair tumbled with sleep, her lovely dark-lashed eyes wide with puzzlement.

'I believe you, child, don't look so fretted. But I'm proud to work for your pa. Why, he's had experts from all over the world here to look at his paintings, and to buy them. You ain't never seen any before?'

Bewildered, Jane shook her head. 'I don't know. The one in the hall, a man and his boat, seemed familiar, but—'

Ellen laughed. 'Sure, you've seen it in the papers. Some posh magazine came about a year ago, and took photographs of 'em all. Why, the name of Augustus Ritchie is known all over the world.'

'Augustus – Augustus – of course!' Jane whispered. 'What a fool I've been!' She had seen reproductions of his vivid depictions of islands, colourful landscapes in an un-mistakable style that was labelled 'primitive' by all the experts, The name Richie had caught her eye too, but that was all. She would never have dreamed that it was her own father who had . . .

'Why sure, his name's John, but his other name's Augustus, leastways it must be ' Ellen sighed, her face kindly as she flip-flopped over the floor to put the plate before Jane. 'You do have a lot to learn about your pa, don't you? An' he's happy you're here, I can see that. I'm glad you came.'

'Thank you, Ellen.' Jane smiled at her, aware of the sudden bond of shared empathy. She wondered fleetingly if Aunt Dorothy had known all these things. Perhaps she would never find out. It suddenly didn't seem important any more. England was so far away, so remote as almost to be another world. She bent to her food as Ellen padded away to make a drink.

After the meal, which was delicious, they sat and drank tea together.

'I'm wide awake,' confessed Jane. 'Is it safe to go for a walk in the garden?'

Ellen laughed. 'Safe? It's safe enough. There's no bur-glars on Saramanca, honey, but are you sure? It's nearly twelve.'

'Quite sure,' Jane nodded. 'Otherwise I'll never get to sleep.'

Ellen shrugged, making clear her opinion about mad English girls who wanted to go walking at night. 'I'll get you a torch. Your pa would never forgive me if you fell and hurt yourself. And don't stray too far from the house, you promise?'

'I promise, Ellen. I'd just like some fresh air.'

'Then you go right up and put a coat over your nightie.

It's cool out. I'll find that old torch.'

Happy, Jane darted quickly up the stairs. She would go down the drive towards the road, then back. It would help to clear her thoughts too. She had too much to take in yet for her ever to get to sleep. Too much startling information to digest – as well as a rich meal.

A few minutes later, guided by the reluctant Ellen, who hovered at the door like a mother hen, Jane set off walking slowly across the verandah, down the steps, and along the wide drive towards the gate. Faintly came Ellen's voice, hushed so as not to disturb her sleeping employer: 'I'll leave the door wide, and the light on.'

Jane waved an acknowledgement and turned away. The gravel crunched beneath her feet, and faint scents of flowers were all around her as she made her slow way along. The air was cool, and she was glad of the light linen coat she'd donned. Torch in hand, she paused, standing in dark shadow away from the house to let her eyes adjust to the darkness.

There was something so peaceful and beautiful about the night that she was loath to disturb it by switching on the torch. The sky was of rich black velvet, diamond-studded. For a full minute Jane gazed up, lost in wonder at the brilliance of the stars twinkling so many miles, so many aeons away. The faint radiance of a thin sickle moon gave enough light for her to see her path. Casting deep sharp shadows, it lent an air of mystery and enchantment to the garden. Jane breathed deeply, a tingle of sheer happiness spreading within her. There had been no mistake, she knew that now. This was right. She had come thousands of miles to be here, and all the doubt and pain were vanished. Her father wanted her. That was all that mattered now.

Slowly, treading carefully so as not to disturb the sleeping night, Jane walked on, lost in a sensation of well-being. Then suddenly all was shattered. A huge black shape bounded out of the darkness towards her, and she saw, with horror, a black dog with bared fangs blocking her path. Frozen with fear, her mood of well-being rudely sundered, Jane faced him, sensing that to run would be dangerous.

'Carlo! Stay!' A man's voice came from the gateway. With a low whine the dog subsided and lay at Jane's feet. Trembling, fumbling for the switch, she clicked on the torch to see Gavin Grant striding towards her from the gate.

CHAPTER TWO

'I'M sorry if he frightened you. He wouldn't have hurt you.'

Jane's heart was thudding so loudly that she barely heard the words. She managed to find her voice as the tall dark man stopped in front of her, and all her dislike of him came rushing back, intensified by the fear that was only now subsiding.

'Does he always leap out at people like that?' she asked, her voice ragged.

'No, he doesn't. But then he doesn't usually see anyone at this time of night.' His voice was even, a dark brown voice that at any other time she would have found attractive. Because of what had happened, and because it belonged to 'that man', Jane felt her hackles rise. An arrogant thread ran through it. Perhaps, she thought wildly, no one ever answers him back.

'I must remember to ask your permission before I take a stroll at night again,' she answered, and turning, began to walk back to her father's house.

Another torch beam crossed her own, a bright yellow spear stabbing the dark. 'You're staying here?' The question was abrupt, puzzled – dismayed.

'Yes,' Jane said shortly. 'Good night.'

There was a muffled exclamation, then: 'You're *John's* daughter?'

She turned back. What did she detect in those words? Whatever it was, they had sounded almost insulting.

'I am.' Jane was shivering. She didn't know why, but if she stayed there any longer, talking to the man, she was sure she would say something quite regrettable. She couldn't understand the strange effect he had on her, but she knew she had never met anyone who could arouse such primitive feelings of fury inside her. It shocked and dismayed her, used as she was to a calm, ordered existence, to discover that she was capable of such fiery dislike. And strangely enough, it was as if he sensed it too. There was in his voice that which puzzled her. She couldn't see him clearly, only the dark outline of him near her, tall, broad-shouldered, powerful, and as he spoke again, she knew what it was.

'I'm Gavin Grant, your father's neighbour, Miss Richie,' the cool dark voice said. 'I hope we'll meet again under more fortunate circumstances. Shall I walk you to the door?'

'No, thanks. As long as you keep your dog away from me, I think I can manage.' Jane turned away and walked up towards the front door, which was a welcoming sight indeed. Shakenly she seemed to hear a mocking echo of his words as she went. There had been something else beside surprise in his voice – a faint threat of what seemed to be contempt. Jane felt her face flame in the cool darkness. How dared he? Who was *he* to speak so?

He was one neighbour she had every intention of avoiding as much as possible. First at Gaver airport, and now this. The man was impossible! Jane, who had been too repressed by Aunt Dorothy ever to actively dislike anyone, or express emotions, now found herself seething inwardly at his insufferable arrogance. The less that she saw of *him*, she realized, the better.

Jane slept late the next morning, until nearly ten. After washing and dressing, she went quickly, guiltily down, looking forward to being able to talk to her father. There was so much wasted time ... As she neared the large lounge where she had met him for the first time the previous day, she heard men's voices, and paused. So he had a visitor. Jane bit her lip and smoothed back her long dark hair, neatly caught in a ribbon for coolness. She wore a simple blue cotton dress that she had made herself. A sleeveless shift, it emphasized her slender figure and youthful feminine curves, and although she could not know it, she looked cool and beautiful in a serene way that was devastating in its effect. Nervously she paused, lightly tapped the door, then went in.

Her father held out his hand as she went towards him. 'Jane, my dear, I've been hearing all about your unfortunate adventure—' and as Jane went to him, she knew before she turned that the man now standing up by the other chair was Gavin Grant.

'Good morning, Miss Ritchie.' She looked at him then, her hand still holding her father's.

'Good morning, Mr. Grant.' It was the first time that she had seen him properly, close to. She saw the grey eyes that appraised her coolly from under level black brows. His face was hard, his chin square and deeply cleft. The black hair that grew in a peak over his forehead was neat, but a shade too long, and his mouth was wide and sensual with a touch of cruelty. He held out his hand and she took it reluctantly, feeling the hard grip of leashed muscular strength. A powerful, dangerous man, instinct told her, with a veiled dislike in his regard that was both puzzling and disturbing.

'That's it,' her father squeezed her other hand. 'And none of this formality, eh? Isn't she lovely, Gavin, my daughter?'

Gavin Grant bowed slightly, mockingly. 'Indeed. I came to apologize for what happened last night – Jane.'

Did she imagine the faint pause before that last word?

'It's quite all right.' She managed to smile, then sat down beside her father. Gavin waited until she was seated before he himself sat again, carelessly crossing his immaculately clad legs before settling back.

'Ellen will have breakfast ready for you, Jane,' John said, apparently unaware of any tension in the air. 'We let you sleep on after your tiring journey. And then Gavin came to see me before going to town, and we got talking ...' Jane listened, nodding in all the right places as the two men spoke. Inwardly she longed to escape. All her senses were tuned to a fine pitch of awareness of the man who sat talking and laughing with her father. It was as if waves of tension spread out across the room to touch her and enfold her with suffocating intensity. He too was aware of it. She sensed his eyes upon her, even now, when she looked at her father, and a pulse beat in her throat. He was in his thirties, a lean powerful figure with the strength to crush her with one hand if he chose. Yet his manners were perfect. Why then, she wondered, did she feel this deep awareness of his power? It was absurd. With an effort, she said, during a pause: 'I'll go and get my breakfast, Father. I don't like to keep Ellen waiting. If you'll excuse me?' Her smile included them both, but it was only for her father. She stood and went towards the door, and Gavin, moving more swiftly, opened it for her.

'Thank you.' Their eyes met, and clashed, and the hostility was there, subtly veiled – but clear to Jane. Perversely, she was annoyed. Why did he dislike her so? He had no right – no reason, surely? It was very disconcerting to know that someone disliked you – even if you disliked *them*. Jane made her way to the kitchen, not a little dismayed at the turn of events.

All was apparently forgotten later, as, walking slowly with her father, she went round the extensive gardens surrounding the villa. She received a pleasant surprise when they reached the end, in a thick grove of dark trees, and her father said: 'Listen. Hear it?'

Faintly came the muted roar of the sea, and she turned to him in delight. 'I didn't realize we were so near!'

'Pity we can't see it from the house – but there, you can't have everything.' He nodded towards his left. 'Gavin sometimes gives beach parties. I must drop a few hints.'

'Not on my account, please,' begged Jane quickly. Too quickly, for her father gave her a speculative look.

'Hmm, so I wasn't mistaken before. Did I detect a certain coolness?'

Jane shook her head. 'Oh, Father, I'm sorry. I didn't mean—'

Her father laughed. She looked quickly at him, dismayed. Had she been *so* obvious?

'Oh, child, don't look so nervous. I was only joking! He is rather overpowering, even I know that. But he's a splendid fellow when you get to know him. He was really sorry about his dog scaring you. That's why he came round to apologize.'

There was so much that Jane could have said, but she held her tongue. Clearly her father admired Gavin Grant. They were neighbours and friends. And she, who had only just arrived, was virtually a stranger. There were many things she had to know about her father, about the missing years. So much to talk about – and Gavin was no part of that. How could she dare to say that she found him intensely arrogant – that she would never forget his behaviour at the airport?

She smiled to reassure her father, and said: 'I'm sure

he's very nice – I'm just being silly. Please let's forget it. I want to know about you. Why didn't you mention about your paintings in any of your letters?'

'Ah!' John gave a deep sigh. 'Ellen told me she'd been talking to you last night. I didn't mention it because I wanted you to come here to see me – your father – not some silly artist.'

'I would have come anyway,' Jane whispered. They went to sit on a bench in the shelter of tall rustling palms, the sharp spiky leaves making vivid outlines against that hard blue sky. The air was heavy with the scent of mimosa and honeysuckle, and everything was so beautiful and colourful that Jane's heart ached. She breathed tremulously. 'I never imagined it would be like this,' she said softly. 'And I never knew you'd written until a month ago.'

John looked down to where his foot idly traced a pattern in the sandy soil. 'I knew Dorothy hated me, but I never imagined she would stoop quite so low. When she wrote—'

'She wrote to you?' Jane couldn't stop the startled words.

'Why, yes! Don't tell me it was without your knowledge?' It was his turn to look stunned.

'When was this? I knew nothing.'

'About two years ago when I was settled here. She wrote and told me not to bother you. You didn't want anything to do with me, and I was wasting my time writing.'

'Oh, no!' Jane's lip trembled. 'Oh, no! But – but you still kept on writing, after that?'

'I had to. I thought that one day you might forgive an old man—'

'No, don't say it, please,' the tears trembled on her lashes. 'Father, I don't understand why she did these

36

things – perhaps I never will – but I swear that if I had ever had one of your letters, I would have answered it.'

'I know that now, child.' He patted her hand. 'And I'll tell you one more thing before we close a painful subject. When I left your mother, it was because she told me to go. I loved her – but I realize now, in the years I've had to think about it, that it was Dorothy who turned her against me. In a sense it was she who broke up our marriage. And I know now why.'

'Did she – was she in l-love with you?' Jane asked slowly.

'I can only imagine so, yes. We met on holiday in St. Ives, twenty years ago. I was thirty-five, poor, trying to paint but getting nowhere, and I met these two sisters who'd gone down together. Dorothy was thirty then, your mother five years younger. We got talking, in the way people do on holiday. I could see then that Dorothy was the dominant sister. I was attracted very much to Lucy your mother, and we went out several times, sometimes with Dorothy, sometimes, if we could manage it, without her. I think she thought that as she was the nearer in age, it should have been her I wanted. She was pretty enough – but even then there was something about her I didn't like. When I asked your mother to marry me, I was honest with her. I said I'd get a job, but painting was my first love – she understood, your mother, but Dorothy refused to.' He paused, eyes looking straight ahead, but unseeing, as if he was living the past again. 'As you know, their old house was big enough for several families, and the two sisters had been living there alone since your grandparents died. It was common sense for Lucy and me to settle down there. We divided the house virtually into two—' Jane nodded, seeing again, as he was, the big old Victorian mansion where she had lived all her life on the outskirts of London, '—and Lucy and I were happy. At first,' he paused again, a look of pain in his eyes. 'Then Dorothy began to cause trouble. Lucy was expecting you, and perhaps this triggered off her jealousy, for she realized that her chances of marriage were slipping by with each year that passed. Gradually the atmosphere changed. After you were born, things improved for a while. Lucy had her baby, and was too busy to listen to her sister. But as you got older, your mother became more and more influenced by Dorothy. I was out at work all day, as a commercial artist in an advertising agency. I could only do my painting at weekends. Dorothy had all the time she wanted to get at your mother – and she did. At first it was small things like, "He says he's working late at the office, but they all say that, don't they?" then it was, "He thinks more of his painting than he does of you," – gradually wearing away at Lucy's resistance until she began to see me as an ogre. It was making you unhappy too. When you were nearly six, there was a big row one day, and you overheard. I was shattered, seeing your face, knowing what it must be doing to you. I told Lucy we were leaving to get a home of our own, just the three of us – and she told me to go – alone.' He put his head in his hands, deeply moved. In a quieter, muffled voice, he went on: 'And, God help me, I went. I just packed up and left.'

Jane put her hand on his shoulders. 'Don't, Daddy. Don't say any more.'

'Yes, just this. I was going to come home for you when I settled here. But then this stupid illness of mine came, and Mac, my doctor, forbade me to travel far. I prayed that you would write – and my prayers were answered.'

There was silence for a few minutes after that. Jane could see so many things now. And although she was shocked and unhappy at the bitterness that must have caused her aunt's actions, somehow it was no surprise to her. Now, even more, she rejoiced that she had come at last.

'Let's go back, Father,' she said quietly after a while. 'I just want to tell you I'm so happy to be here.'

Slowly they walked back to the house. A burden had lifted from John's shoulders. He walked with a new air, and Jane knew the telling of the truth had done him good, and brought him peace of mind.

Later that day, John showed Jane the car that had been in the garage for six months, unused. It was a new Ford Taunus, a beautiful silver blue in colour.

'Can you drive, Jane?' he asked. She shook her head regretfully.

'No. Don't you?'

He shrugged. 'Not – recently. Would you like to learn?'

'I – I don't know,' she hesitated. 'I think so, but I've never tried.'

'I'll ask Gavin to teach you—' he began, but she made a wordless exclamation, and he chuckled. 'No? Sorry. Perhaps Megan, or her son Colin, I'm sure he'd love to.'

'Well, I'd certainly give it a try. What about a licence?'

He laughed. 'Oh, you don't need one here. You just set off. There are so few cars on the island it doesn't matter.'

They went back to the house, and Jane phoned the American, Jackson, as she had promised. She also sent a cablegram to her aunt to say she had arrived safely. Even after all she had heard, it was impossible just to cut the woman completely out of her life.

That evening, after dinner, Jane and her father sat

together in the living room and talked. The purple-black sky was full of diamond-bright stars, and the french windows were open, letting in cool scented night air.

'Go and get the guitar,' John asked. 'You promised you'd play to me.' Jane had changed into a cool blue trouser suit. She brought the guitar in and sat in her favourite position for playing, cross-legged on the polished wooden floor. After a few minutes' strumming, she began one of her favourite songs: 'Those Were the Days,' and unselfconsciously began to sing as she picked out the sad plaintive melody.

She could not know what an appealing figure she made, sat there on the floor, her long dark hair flowing free, her oval face intent on the instrument she cradled, her dark lashes fanning her cheeks. She was lost in a world she loved, a world of melody. And her father watched, his face rapt, as he listened to her low sweet voice, clear and pure, and the liquid notes that spilled out into the night.

The last sounds died away, and there was silence. Then a voice came from the direction of the window, and Gavin Grant stepped into the room, his eyes dark and compelling on Jane.

'That was beautiful,' he said, and his voice was quiet.

She drew breath sharply, and jumped to her feet, suddenly selfconscious. John turned. 'Why, Gavin! How long have you been there?'

'I was about to knock when I heard the guitar. I thought it was you playing, John, so I came round the back to listen. I heard it all the way through.' He turned to Jane. 'I must congratulate you. You play well.'

'Thank you.' She looked directly at him, wondering if there was any trace of sarcasm in his tone, but he seemed quite sincere. She was glad that she hadn't known he was there, but at the same time obscurely resented the fact that he had listened. She hadn't played for him, but for her father.

Gavin turned to John, who waved him to a chair. 'I've come with an invitation, John, from Sara and her mother.'

John raised his eyebrows, and Gavin laughed. 'Look, I'm only the messenger. They're giving a party on Saturday, and wonder if you and Jane would like to go?'

John looked at his daughter. 'Well, Jane, how about it? How many are going, Gavin?'

The dark man shrugged. 'As far as I can gather, just a couple of dozen.'

And Jane suddenly remembered Megan's words the previous day. She had said that Leonie and Sara would be very keen to meet her – especially because Sara, who was apparently after Gavin, did not like competition. That's rich, thought Jane, repressing a smile. Did they but know it, she was no danger to them at all. The dislike was mutual, even if, she mused, he had seemed almost *pleasant* a few moments ago, when he had praised her guitar-playing.

She looked up from the guitar. 'It sounds very nice,' she answered. Gavin looked across at her. Could he read thoughts? she wondered. He had a shrewd grey gaze that seemed to bore through her. Jane realized with a sudden shock just how attractive his eyes were. She had never noticed before.

But he spoke casually enough. 'Fine. I'll phone them and say you'll be going. I'll run you both, of course.'

'That's good of you,' John said. 'I think I'll enjoy it, you know.'

'Then that's settled.' Gavin looked at his watch. 'Well, I mustn't stay. I only came to—'

41

'Nonsense, have a drink. What'll it be – whisky? Martini?'

'A whisky, please. Just a little soda.'

'I'll get it.' Jane stood and went to the drinks cabinet in the corner by the french window.

'I'll have a drop of whisky as well,' her father said.

She took the men their drinks and sat down again. Gavin raised an inquiring eyebrow. 'Aren't you having one?'

'I don't drink,' she answered. It took a strong effort of will to remain in the room with him there, but Jane had vowed to herself that she would not give her father any cause to think her bad-mannered. The two men were friends. While she was there she would curb her instinctive dislike and make the effort to be sociable, however difficult it might be. So they were going to a party – and Gavin was taking them. That too she would put up with – but only for her father's sake, for he was clearly delighted with the invitation.

Gavin raised his glass to them both. 'Your good health,' he said. 'You're a very unusual person, Jane. I didn't know there were any girls who didn't drink nowadays.'

A beautiful retort came to her lips, but she bit it hastily back, and merely smiled sweetly. At that moment Ellen came in.

'Mrs. Davis is here, Mr. Ritchie,' she said.

In walked Megan, followed by a tall, good-looking, fair-haired young man who could only be her son, so alike were they. And Jane's eyes met those of the young man, a startling blue, with an indefinable spark in them that caused her heart to skip a beat. He's nice, she thought.

Megan introduced them, and Colin held Jane's hand a fraction of a second longer than necessary. He smiled at her, 'Hello, Jane.'

42

'Hello, Colin,' she felt a warm glow as his eyes caressed her. Reluctantly, it seemed, he released her hand, and turned to Gavin who was, Jane noted, watching them both with a cynical amusement to his mouth.

'Evening, Gavin. I didn't see you.'

'So I noticed,' Gavin's tone was dry, and Jane felt herself go pink. How dared he! She added 'patronizing' to her mental list of that man's faults. He went on smoothly, addressing both Megan and Colin: 'You've saved me a job. Leonie asked me to invite you both to her party on Saturday.'

Colin looked at Jane. 'You're going?' There was a wealth of meaning in his words.

'Yes,' she answered.

'Good. All right, Mother?'

Megan smiled round at them all. 'Of course. It should be very interesting.' And her eyes met Jane's in a look that clearly said: 'There, what did I tell you?'

John Ritchie beamed. 'This gets better every minute. Jane dear, see what Megan and Colin will have to drink.'

She found Colin at her side as she poured the drinks for him and his mother. When they were seated again, the three men were near to one another, and Megan and Jane were in adjoining seats, so that they were able to talk unheard. Megan said quietly: 'Jane, you remember what I told you?'

Jane glanced discreetly to where Gavin sat, drink in hand. He was leaning forward, making a point to John and Colin, and certainly would not overhear.

'Yes, I remember,' she answered quietly, wondering what was coming, sensing something disturbing in Megan's manner.

The older woman kept her voice low. 'May I give you a

43

word of friendly advice?'

'Please do,' and Jane smiled at her, liking this woman more each time she saw her.

'Well, it's just this. They'll be frightfully charming, and I'm sure you'll have an enjoyable evening, but this is more than just a party—' she paused and sipped her drink, as if wondering how to put something. Jane waited, some instinct telling her what was to come. Megan went on: 'It's a "weighing up" session. I'm sorry to put it so crudely, but—' she looked up as a lull came in the men's conversation, and finished in a louder tone: 'Tell you what, Jane, let's go up to your room and pick something to wear, shall we?'

'That seems a good idea.' Jane fell in with the little plan immediately, too intrigued to do otherwise. Megan smiled brilliantly at the three men.

'Do excuse us, gentlemen. Girl talk.' She held out her hand. 'Come along, Jane, I'm sure these three can gossip more comfortably without us,' and they sailed out of the room, watched by the now silent men.

Upstairs, Megan kicked off her shoes and sat on the edge of the bed, after carefully putting her glass down on the glass-topped bedside table. 'Ah, that's better!' she began to laugh, her voice low and attractive. 'I'm sorry, love, but I couldn't have kept quiet a moment longer.'

Jane sat beside her. 'I know. Do go on, I'm all agog.'

Megan's blue eyes rested thoughtfully on Jane. 'You know, I think you and I are going to get on splendidly.'

'You say it as if you didn't think so before.' Jane's voice reflected her puzzlement. There was something she didn't understand here.

Megan shook her head as if annoyed with herself. 'Tch! I'm sorry. You've put me in my place—'

'I'm sorry, Megan, I didn't mean—' Jane began

anxiously.

'No, don't apologize. You're quite right, love. I'm going to tell you something now, because whatever my faults, I'll admit to my mistakes – and I made one, quite unintentionally, about you.'

Jane waited. A tingle of apprehension warned her that her unwitting words had triggered off something that was going to explain what had been puzzling her about several things.

Megan closed her eyes for a moment, then began: 'When your father told us you were coming, after so many years, I'm afraid we all jumped to the rather uncharitable conclusion that you were—' she hesitated, and Jane prompted softly:

'Go on.' She sat still, her hands clasped on her lap, a cold sensation of dismay spreading and growing inside her, for she knew now. But she had to hear it *said*, had to know properly.

'Well, Jane, that you were only coming because you'd discovered your father was a wealthy man – therefore out for what you could get.' At Jane's wordless exclamation of anguish, Megan reached out a small hand and touched the girl's arm. 'Forgive me, but I must finish, if only to let you see how wrong and stupid people can be. We thought you'd ignored him all these years, and then, when he's ill, and given up painting, thus automatically increasing the value of the existing ones, you decided to arrive. That's why I was so puzzled when you were obviously surprised at the sight of your father's house. I knew by your face that it was genuine – and it was then I began to think that perhaps *we* had been mistaken.'

Jane sat there in silence for a moment. There was something else she had to know. 'Megan, who is "we?" '

Megan's face was contrite. 'Why, all of us. Myself – Gavin—'

'So that's why!'

'Why what?'

Jane turned to the older woman. 'You remember I told you about Gavin at the airport?' Megan nodded. 'Well,' Jane continued, 'when we met, he was almost – horrible – as though *he* hated *me*. I d-didn't know why – just thought he was like that with everybody, but now I realize. He thinks I'm a little gold-digger, doesn't he, just out for what I can get?'

Megan moved uncomfortably. 'He's very forthright, I'm afraid, Jane.'

Jane nodded. 'I could use stronger words than that to describe him. I'm going to tell you something, Megan—' and she began to tell the other the whole story of her discovery about her father's existence, beginning with the request from the new postman that had triggered off the chain of events, even remembering what had been said by her aunt about her father living in a beach shanty.

When she had finished there was utter silence. Then at last Megan spoke: 'You poor child! What can I say?'

Jane managed a wan smile. 'Nothing. I just wanted you to know, for I don't want you to think badly of me, Megan.'

'Oh, my dear!' Megan put her hands to her face in dismay. 'That I could have ever harboured such uncharitable thoughts—'

'Don't. You were nice to me, even so,' Jane insisted.

'When I tell Gavin what you've told me, he—'

'No!' Jane determinedly cut in. 'I don't want you to tell him!'

'I don't understand!' Megan's voice reflected sheer bewilderment. 'I must do!'

46

Jane shook her head. 'No, you mustn't. In fact I want you to promise me.'

'But why?'

Jane struggled for words. 'Because – because I despise him. He thinks I'm a gold-digger – let him continue to think so. I don't care a jot about his opinion of me. He's arrogant and overbearing – and I don't think I've ever met anyone I've disliked so much in my life!' Her mouth trembled slightly. 'I know he's a friend of my father's, and for that reason only I'll try and be polite towards him, but to think that he dared to assume all these things you've told me were true, and treat me with that contempt—' as Megan would have protested, she went on: 'Oh yes, he has. It's there in his manner, in the way he looks at me, and speaks. I d-didn't understand why, but now I do – and it somehow makes him so much worse. Only my father knows the truth – and now you, Megan, and I've told you all this in confidence. Please keep it like that.'

'I think,' said Megan very slowly, 'I'm beginning to understand you. But it seems so awful for me to know, and not be able to—'

'But that's how I want it,' Jane insisted. 'I've lived for six years with an aunt who is just the same as him. Her opinions are right, and anyone who disagrees is wrong – it's as simple as that. To her, my father was wicked because he left my mother. The fact that it was she who drove him away doesn't count. I'm only just beginning to discover just how wrong she is herself about things. I put up with it for six years – I can surely cope with that man Gavin Grant for a while. If he can't learn to judge others by what they *are* – not what *he* thinks they are, then as far as I'm concerned, he's not worth knowing.'

'And can't you find a little charity in your heart for him, Jane?' Megan asked softly. 'You've opened my eyes tonight. You have a depth of understanding far beyond your years. Can you not find it in your heart to try and understand him?'

'No.' Jane was adamant. 'Promise me, Megan.'

'I have no choice. Of course you have my word, Jane.'

'Thank you.' The two women looked at each other; in the younger one's eyes was a brave defiance that Megan could only reluctantly admire. She smiled slowly. 'I hope you know what you're doing,' she said, 'so we'll say no more about it. Now—' she looked briskly round the room, 'we originally came for a girlish heart-to-heart about the party.'

Jane laughed. 'It seems a bit superfluous now, doesn't it? Weren't you going to warn me that Sara might consider me a "rival"? It hardly applies after all we've discussed.'

'Well, not quite,' Megan smiled ruefully. 'You see, I was going to tell you – and I couldn't downstairs – that Sara, in spite of all her charm, will – very subtly, I grant you – try and make you look foolish. Now, she'll do it in one of two ways – and don't forget, I know her very well, so you can take this as gospel. She'll either ring you before Saturday, and tell you not to wear anything elaborate, just "any old thing", or she won't warn you at all, in which case you'll go dressed as nicely as possible, to find all the other guests wearing frightfully casual clothes, so that you will feel – and look – overdressed.'

Jane took a deep breath. 'Wow! Lovely people!'

Megan smiled. 'As you say, lovely people. They've done it before, and they'll do it again. This time you won't be alone, I'll help you.'

'Thank you,' Jane said simply. 'Shall I let you know if she rings me?'

'Yes. We'll take it from there. Have you any nice dresses?'

Jane opened the wardrobe door. 'Not really. I gathered together as many cool dresses as I could – but I've never really had many clothes. Aunt Dorothy couldn't afford any – and I've only just left school.'

'Mmm,' Megan looked thoughtful. 'I think we'll have a word with your father. There's only the one big store in Port Patrick – Gavin's, of course. But he'll have plenty in, he always does.'

'What? Gavin's what? I missed that.'

'What! You didn't know? Gavin owns the big store in the only town on Saramanca – also, incidentally, its two hotels.'

'I didn't know,' Jane confessed. 'But then I never asked.'

Megan laughed. 'He's worth a fortune, love. His father practically put this place on the map. It's all Gavin's now, and I must say he has his father's flair. And *that's* why dear Sara is trying so hard.' She closed the wardrobe door firmly. 'Let's go down,' then she paused and added: 'Just one little word of advice before we go. You–er–weren't by any chance thinking of teaching Gavin a lesson, were you?'

'Heavens, no!' Jane answered, startled.

Megan nodded. 'That's all right. It was just a thought. Only I was going to warn you if so. He's all steel. He's tough – very tough. And he can be – and frequently is – ruthless, as anyone who has ever crossed swords with him can tell you.' She smiled. 'Even though I like him, I'm aware of that. Come on, love.'

Jane's head was whirling as they went down. Although she had denied vehemently Megan's suggestion, she now wondered. Had the faintest childish thought of revenge been in the back of her mind? She was no longer sure.

CHAPTER THREE

THE next day was Friday. As Jane was about to go downstairs to breakfast, the telephone shrilled. Ellen called: 'It's for you, Jane.' and padded back to the kitchen. Jane ran lightly down the stairs.

'Hello?' For a moment she wondered if it was Megan, then heard a high sweet feminine voice say:

'Jane? Hello, this is Sara Smythe. I hope I may call you Jane?'

'Why, yes. Hello, Sara.' A tingle ran up her spine.

'I was just calling to welcome you to Saramanca, and to say thanks for accepting our party invitation tomorrow.'

'Thank you for asking us,' Jane answered, heartbeats subsiding as she calmed herself.

'Mother and I are so looking forward to meeting you,' the voice continued. 'Social life gets a bit boring here sometimes, it's lovely to see a new face. I just called to tell you, actually, not to bother dressing up tomorrow. The party will be quite casual – so much nicer that way, don't you think?'

'Why, yes,' Jane agreed. So it was happening. In spite of Megan's warning, she hadn't really believed that anyone could deliberately do such an unkind trick. She was, she reflected, having her eyes opened to the strange ways people could behave. Perhaps Sara, this sweet-voiced creature on the phone, was well matched with Gavin. Two of a kind indeed!

Sara was going on about how much she was looking forward to meeting Jane, and was assured the feeling was mutual.

She hung up thoughtfully when at last the other girl said good-bye. Now she must phone Megan and tell her. Ellen showed Jane where to find Megan's number, and Jane dialled it. The older woman began to laugh when she heard Jane's voice.

'Hello. I knew it would be you. So she's rung. What's it to be? Casual?'

'Yes.'

'I'll be right over. You've just phoned in time. I was going to Port Patrick myself for some things. Have you had breakfast?'

'No, but it won't take me long.'

'Don't hurry, love. No one ever does here. 'Bye.'

Jane realized something as she went into the kitchen. The invitation had been delivered by Gavin the previous evening. Had he then phoned to tell Sara and her mother of the acceptance? Or had he gone back to see Sara, and tell her in person? It was of no importance, and yet Jane found herself wondering. Wondering too, very fleetingly, if he knew of his girl-friend's twisted sense of humour regarding party invitations.

Half an hour later she and Megan were travelling swiftly down the dazzling white wide road to the other side of the island. Megan looked youthful and attractive in white sleeveless tunic top over blue trousers. A white chiffon scarf held her blonde hair back in a bunch, and she looked cool and elegant. Jane, in a blue patterned terylene dress that had been almost too thin in England, was uncomfortably warm in the heat from the fiery morning sun.

Megan noticed her stirring uneasily and gave a sympathetic grin. 'Synthetics are awkward in this climate,' she admitted. 'Cotton's always the best. Still, your dad's

51

given us a free hand. We'll soon have you fitted out for this heat!'

'I feel guilty about using his account,' Jane confessed. 'I'm not going to spend much.'

'Nonsense!' Megan's voice was firm. 'He told me you were to have exactly what you wanted. He's glad of the opportunity, believe me, Jane. Anyway,' she added, 'you can't let me down. I've never had a daughter to choose clothes with. You wouldn't want to disappoint an elderly matron, would you?'

Her laughter was genuine and unaffected, and Jane felt a surge of happiness that not even thoughts of Gavin could spoil. They were going to the shop he owned, but there was little likelihood of seeing him, Megan had assured her before they set off. Now she said, as if just remembering: 'Colin says he'll try and meet us for coffee in the restaurant. He's very taken with you – or had you noticed?'

Jane smiled, giving her a sidelong glance. 'What do I say to that without seeming conceited?' But the warm glow filled her again.

'Nothing.' Megan's laugh bubbled out again. 'Just relax and enjoy it. I must warn you – though he'd kill me if he knew – that Colin is a bit of a flirt. It might just do him good to meet a girl who doesn't fall over herself to go out with him.'

'I'll try and remember,' Jane promised. Inwardly, though, she wondered what Megan would say if she knew that she had never had a boy-friend, had never even, at the ripe old age of eighteen, been kissed. Aunt Dorothy had done her work well, she thought wryly. Without putting too much into words, she had managed to instil in Jane such doubts that she had been painfully unsure of herself. Now, it was as if she were released from prison.

The heady excitement of knowing she could attract a member of the opposite sex was a new and wonderful feeling. She hugged it to herself. Now was not the time to reveal it. Perhaps soon, when her new-found confidence was established and sure, she would be able to tell Megan, and perhaps even make a joke of it.

Yet Jane did not realize the extent of Megan's own shrewdness, the other woman's instinctive knowledge of Jane's naïvety, her motherly desire to help the girl she was beginning to like so much. Nor did Jane realize something else that Megan sensed. That her very innocent shyness was a deep compelling attraction on its own; that combined with her serene beauty, as yet unawakened, Jane had a devastating potential. She would be, thought Megan, a beautiful and exciting woman – and very soon too.

The sky was almost white, the light so brilliant that it hurt the eyes, and to either side of them were the inevitable palms, curving elegantly against the dazzling background. In the distance, faintly, mountains soared effortlessly upwards, misty, blue. Jane took a deep breath. 'This place is so beautiful,' she whispered.

'And unspoilt, that's what's so unusual. Oh, we get tourists of course, mainly in Port Patrick. A cruise liner stops every fortnight, and the passengers come ashore and spent lots of money buying lace and wood carvings – and everyone's happy. But generally we're quiet. That's how I like it, and how Gavin intends it to stay.'

That man again! Was there no getting away from his opinions? Jane wondered. But she said nothing. Soon they neared the town, the houses were clustered more thickly, and were slightly smaller than the villas they had left behind. Rich gardens lent bursts of colour as they swept past on the wide road, bordered with white pavements and a criss-cross of side roads. And everywhere was the impression of space, and a slow unhurriedness that added to the charm of the town. Distantly water gleamed in the wide sweeping bay as they went down a slope into Port Patrick's main street. There were shops now, and people of all shades of colour, gaily or simply clad, going about their business with none of the bustle to be found in larger cities. A white-coated policeman waved them on, after letting an ancient bus through, and Megan said: 'That's the island bus. It passes your father's house twice a day – not that you'll need it, I don't imagine. He'll lend you the car whenever you want it, I'm sure.'

'I can't drive,' confessed Jane. 'But I'd like to learn.'

'That you shall! Colin or I will show you. We'll fix something up for you. How long are you staying, Jane?'

'I planned on a month, but—' and here Jane paused.

Megan prompted her, 'Has your father asked you to stay longer?'

'Yes.'

'And do you want to?' Megan gave her an amused side-long glance.

'I – don't know. Of course I *do*, but—'

'But you have doubts. Is it your aunt? A boy-friend?'

Jane laughed. 'Not a boy-friend, no, but I promised my aunt I would—' she bit her lip, '—try and p-pay her—' She stopped.

'If you want my opinion,' Megan interrupted, her lovely face slightly pink, as if at her own temerity, 'you owe her nothing. After all she's done! Oh, I'm sorry, Jane, it's none of my business, but really!'

'I know.' Jane gave her a reassuring smile. 'It's just that – well, she has no one. I'm beginning to see what a lonely, unhappy woman she is.'

54

'You've only just arrived, love. Wait a week or so, then see how you feel. Perhaps you'll be able to sort something out. In fact, I'm sure you will.' And she turned sharply off the road and into a car park behind a large modern building that seemed to be all windows.

A large sign down the side proclaimed: 'Grant's' in huge red letters.

'This is it. Out we get.'

Inside, the store was cooler, the atmosphere one of quiet, almost old-fashioned elegance. White-coated assistants worked in the supermarket on the ground floor, with its long refrigerated counters piled high with every imaginable food, fresh, tinned, or frozen. Megan led Jane to the lifts. 'We'll get the food later,' she told her. 'First things first.'

They were whisked up to the second floor, and here Jane's feet sank into thick red carpet. She looked around her at the racks of dresses, at the women wandering slowly round, looking, occasionally vanishing into curtained fitting rooms. And here again was the air of unhurried calm that seemed so prevalent on the island. A friendly blue-eyed teenager approached them, dressed in gay cotton shift and thonged sandals on her bare tanned feet.

'Hello, Mrs. Davis. Can I help you?'

'No, thanks, Nonie, not for a while anyway. We're just looking.'

'Help yourselves.' The girl smiled and waved an arm expansively. 'Call me if you need me.'

The next hour passed in a magic haze of looking, trying on, searching – and laughter. Jane had never imagined that buying clothes could be such fun. With her aunt it had been a chore to be over and done with as quickly and cheaply as possible. Now, with Megan busily pulling hems, frowning, considering and consulting, the experience was exhilarating, almost an adventure.

Then they found it – the dress. Even as Megan lifted it from the rack in a secluded corner, Jane knew. It was so very simple, deceptively so, just a plain straight floor-length dress in a brilliant flame-coloured silk. The neck was rounded and low, bordered with a brown band of silk that was embroidered with tiny dark flowers. And the dress was sleeveless.

'Try this one on.' Megan held it up. 'And these other day dresses.' She waved to Nonie, and pointed towards a changing room. The girl nodded, grinning.

As Jane pulled the cool slippery material over her head, she knew that the dress would fit perfectly – and it did. She peeped out to where Megan waited.

'Will you zip me up the back, please?' she called.

Then, that accomplished, she walked slowly towards a long mirror just outside the changing rooms. It didn't need Megan's stunned face to tell her that she looked good. Gently she smoothed the material over her hips, and turned round.

'Why, Jane,' Megan's voice was absolutely delighted, 'you look wonderful – really. I—'

'Yes, she does, Mother.'

Jane whirled to see Colin coming towards them across the floor. His eyes were only for Jane, and she felt warm colour flood her face as she looked at Megan, overcome by sudden shyness.

'What are you doing here?' his mother demanded. 'Shouldn't you be earning your salary?'

Colin flicked back his cuff to consult his watch. 'It's eleven – break time. I've come to take you two ladies for a cold drink.'

'All right.' Megan grinned at Jane. 'Come on, he might

not ask again. Go and change. We'll try on the others later.'

As Jane walked back to the changing room, she heard Megan say: 'And we'll tell Nonie you're having *that* for a start.'

Carefully Jane eased the dress off, then slipped her own dress on again. Her heart was beating fast. It was ridiculous to feel so pleased, she knew – but she had never worn such an exciting garment in her life. In the few minutes that she had had the dress on, she had felt a different person. She had felt almost – beautiful! She chided herself for such conceit, pulled a face at herself in the mirror to bring her back to normal. 'Vain hussy!' she mouthed. But somehow the warm glow remained, and as they sat in a small cool lounge drinking iced coffee and eating sticky sweet cakes, she saw Megan glance at her more than once with a 'we've got a secret', look. Colin was busy telling her about his work at the store, enthusing about his boss, Gavin, and Jane listened and commented in all the right places, well aware of Megan's amusement.

'Where is Gavin?' his mother inquired during a pause, stubbing her cigarette out in a huge shell ashtray on the table.

'Over at one of the hotels this morning. There's a meeting on about something.'

'Well, don't let us keep you, dear,' Megan said. 'Jane and I have a few more things to look at – and I know you're busy.'

Colin pulled a face of mock dismay at Jane. 'She's trying to get rid of me,' he grumbled. 'After I struggled to find time to take you both for coffee too.'

'You make me sound like an ogre,' Megan protested.

It was nice to listen to them, thought Jane. Clearly a

strong bond of affection existed between the two, in spite of all their bantering. She wished, suddenly, that she and her father could be going to the party with them, instead of with Gavin. She knew she would feel so much more confident, having friends to arrive with, instead of that man – who looked at her in a way that sent strange shivers of apprehension up her spine. Despite her confident assertion to Megan the previous night that Gavin's opinions didn't matter a jot, she knew that in a way, she was frightened of him. Even the change in him, when he had caught her playing the guitar – even that, in a way, had been disturbing. He was a deep, complex man. Jane wished fervently that she had never met him. And if she could have known then of the events that would follow the party, she would have been even more sure that to know him was a mistake. But she didn't – fortunately for her peace of mind, so soon to be shattered.

She realized that they were looking at her, and laughed apologetically. 'I'm sorry. Was I miles away? I was just thinking about my – my dress,' she fibbed.

'For tomorrow's party, I gather?' asked Colin gently.

Megan answered for her. 'Yes – but not a word to anyone, understand?'

Colin grinned, 'Ah-hah! Do I detect a subtle plan?'

'You do,' answered Megan crisply.

He traced a pattern idly on the checked tablecloth with his spoon.

'Well, then, ladies, you might just be interested to know that a certain young woman was in this store yesterday afternoon buying a rather special dress for a rather special party.'

Megan gave Jane a level look. 'What did I tell you?' she demanded. Then, to Colin: 'What was it like?'

'Heavens, I haven't a clue,' he protested. 'I only know

because it went on her account. But it cost a bomb, I can tell you *that*.' He grinned wickedly at Jane. 'I shouldn't worry. That orange frock is a knockout.'

Megan winced. 'Not "orange", dear, please. "Exotic flame" is the shade.'

'Sorry.' He looked quite unabashed. 'You must excuse a mere male's ignorance. It looked orange – and quite gorgeous – to me.' He stood up. 'Will you excuse me? Call in at my office before you go and I'll have everything packed ready for you.'

'All right, dear. Bye-bye. Come on, Jane, we'll go too. I think we'll have to buy sandals and a bag – and oh, yes, perhaps a stole of some sort . . .' Jane gave Colin a resigned look, and followed Megan from the lounge.

They spent another half hour in the dress department, and Jane was persuaded that two simple cotton dresses, two pairs of smart shorts, and six cotton tee-shirts, were just right for her wardrobe. Then they went to try on sandals and to look at stoles. Megan showed Jane how to wear the one she had chosen, a fine, almost transparent silk scarf in a deep brown shade, an exact match to the neckband on the dress.

'Well, that's that.' She looked at Jane with satisfaction. 'Now I think we'll get my groceries, and then collect all your things from Colin. Everything will be taken to his office, to go on your father's account. It's on the ground floor.'

As they went down in the self-operated lift, Jane said: 'I don't know how to thank you, Megan.'

Megan laughed. 'Then don't try. I've enjoyed it more than you have, love, I assure you. Will you let me do your hair tomorrow?'

Startled, Jane looked at her. 'But I—' she began.

'Please. I'll tell you a little secret. Years ago, I worked

in a hairdresser's – before I was married, I mean. I've told you, I miss having a daughter to do all these things for. Please say you will. I can just picture you with all that glorious mass swept up high.'

'Then I'd be delighted,' Jane answered. 'But honestly, I've never had it swept up. I don't know if it will suit me.'

'It will, I promise you.'

The two women went into the food department, and Megan loaded a trolley with a week's supply of vegetables, fruit, and meat. A white-coated assistant rushed over when they were at the check-out desk.

'Shall I take these to your car, Mrs. Davis?' he asked, brown face wreathed in smiles.

'Will you, Jason? Thanks so much.'

She was well liked by everybody, Jane guessed. All the staff at the store greeted her with big smiles, and nothing was too much trouble. And, Jane knew, it wasn't just because her son was the manager. There was affection in their manner too, a warmth brought out in response to her own.

Megan took Jane's arm, and they left the supermarket, passed through a toiletries section, where Jane bought sunglasses, then another department which sold books and magazines – Jane was surprised to see all the well-known paperbacks on sale – to reach a door marked: 'Private.'

'It's all right, love,' Megan laughed as she saw Jane's shocked look as she pushed it open. 'I've been here hundreds of times.'

They went through into a corridor that had small offices leading off, white-walled, with glazed windows, and everywhere the hum of the air-conditioning. The clatter of typewriters came from the first two, and Megan knocked at the third door.

'Come in.' But it wasn't Colin who answered. As they went into the large airy office with its clean light furniture, the man sitting at the desk, giving them a surprised glance, was Gavin Grant.

He uncurled his long legs slowly from his seat, flung down a sheaf of papers, and stood up.

'Megan – Jane! This is an unexpected pleasure.' But the smile at his mouth was not for Jane. He had barely glanced at her.

'I'm sorry, Gavin, I thought Colin would be here.' She looked around the room. 'We only came to collect some parcels for Jane. He said he'd have them packed up for us.'

'I see. Well, I only just got back. He had to go and deal with an argument in the stockroom, and I was just checking some statements he asked me to look at. Wait a moment,' he was moving as he spoke. 'These will be what you want, I think.' He went to a filing cabinet in the corner by the window, and lifted a huge box from the top. Inside, on top of the carefully wrapped clothes and sandals, was a bill. He glanced briefly at it, then looked across at them. 'You're right. All these are on John's account. I'll take them to the car for you.'

'Oh, don't trouble, I know you're busy—' began Megan.

'No trouble, I assure you.' He was already striding to the door and opening it for them to go out, the box held securely under one arm. He had tossed the slip of paper on to the desk first.

As Jane passed him, she was conscious of his eyes on her, and felt her neck grow warm. That it should be him here, of all people! And what was he thinking now? Undoubtedly that she was wasting no time in spending her father's money. Let him think what he liked, then! She held her head high as she left the office. All right, so he assumed the worst about her. Good! she thought, it'll give him something else to feel contemptuous about. Perhaps it's lucky for me that I'm not a poor old Chinese woman. At least he can't have *me* marched off to heaven knows where – much as I'm sure he'd like to. In fact, she mused, as they went outside into the dazzling sunlight, he must be feeling very frustrated at not being able to tell me precisely what he thinks of me!

How galling for a man like him to have to curb his tongue, to put on a show of politeness, however meagre, to someone he thinks as badly of as me. I'm delighted!

It must have been the heat, and the intense glare, that was making her eyelids prickle, and the back of her throat feel sore. She blinked furiously to dispel the moisture in her eyes, and decided to wear the sunglasses as soon as possible.

They reached the car, and Gavin placed Jane's box carefully in the boot, beside the carton of food.

'Thanks, Gavin.' Megan felt for her keys. 'We'll see you at Sara's tomorrow, if not before.'

'At Sara's, yes.' He opened the driver's door for Megan, and Jane quickly walked round to her passenger door, determined not to wait for him to open it for her – if indeed he intended to.

They said their goodbyes and drove off. As the car went out, Jane looked back. Gavin stood there watching the car, his expression inscrutable.

'You know something, Jane?' Megan glanced at her as she drove in leisurely fashion along the blinding white road. 'I think I know what you mean about Gavin.'

'You noticed it too?' Jane moistened her dry lips with her tongue.

'I could feel the vibrations, yes. Oh, men! How stupid they are!'

'And he's no doubt examining the bill, and thinking how soon I've got started on spending Father's money,' she answered lightly.

'I do wish you'd let me tell him.'

Jane shook her head. 'No. He can think what he likes about me,' and she looked out of the window, but she saw nothing of the people, only the image of a tall powerful man standing in a sunlit yard, with no expression on his face.

As the time for the party drew nearer, Jane found her nervousness increasing. It was all a big mistake, she knew that now. In spite of Megan's assurances that she would look stunning, Jane knew she lacked the confidence to appear before a crowd of people, and suffer an inspection, however subtle.

Her father had gone to rest in the afternoon, and at five, Megan came to do Jane's hair, just as he came downstairs. He looked pale, and Jane, who had just opened the door for Megan, exclaimed: 'Father, are you all right?'

'I'll be fine in a little while, Jane, don't you worry. I'm just overtired, that's all. I'll have some tea. Ellen knows how to make it just as I like it. Away you girls go – and mind now, I want a preview of this dress, just to see if I approve.'

'You will, Dad,' Jane went to hug him. 'I'll have my hair done, then put it on to show you.'

Upstairs in the bathroom, as she washed her long silky hair, Jane asked Megan, who was sitting comfortably on a stool watching: 'What exactly *is* wrong with my father? He doesn't look at all well today.'

Megan sighed. 'Mac doesn't know. Every so often he

has these "attacks" as he calls them. He loses the use of his arms for several hours. It could be caused by some nervous trouble – in fact that's what Mac thinks it is, so he prescribes sedatives, and rest, with gentle daily exercise. But your father's a stubborn man. That's why Mac is hoping you'll be able to persuade him to see a specialist. He'll be at the party tonight, by the way. I'll introduce you, and you can have a quiet chat while I talk to your dad.'

'All right,' Jane agreed.

Megan had brought a large plastic bag full of curlers, and a hand dryer for Jane's hair. Sitting in the bedroom afterwards, with the dryer whirring softly away, they talked of life on the island, its advantages and its drawbacks. There was little poverty there, with a native population almost exclusively engaged in fishing, growing fruit, sugar and coconuts. There was also a thriving lace-making industry, Saramanca lace being very popular among the tourists from the cruise liners that called. 'You must buy some lace next time you go to Port Patrick,' said Megan. 'I'll help you make it into a dress – or a nightie. It's very versatile, and extremely beautiful. In fact—' she looked thoughtfully at Jane through the mirror, – 'if there'd been time, we could have made you one for the party tonight. It would have looked stunning, white lace over a pink silk slip—'

'Heavens,' Jane protested, 'you've done enough already, Megan.'

'Mm, well, the next one you go to.'

'All right, thank you.' She watched the older woman as she deftly brushed the clean shiny tresses, a look of concentration on her face as she worked out the best way to pin Jane's hair back. And Jane sat very still and quiet. She had showered and changed before Megan came, so that all she had to do was slip on the dress and make up just before they left for the party at night.

Now, seeing that Megan had everything under control, she asked: 'And the disadvantages? It can't *really* be paradise here, can it? Even though it seems so to me.' Except for *that man*, but this was added very quietly, and only in her heart.

Megan smiled and frowned thoughtfully. 'Let me see. Well, we occasionally get very violent storms – really frightening ones, I mean – we get a fair amount of rain, which is unusual for a tropical island, but accounts for the very rich greenness of everything that grows. And we occasionally – and this is very rare, thank goodness – get invaded by millions of nasty little flies. And the only thing to do when that happens is to stay indoors, spray everywhere you can, and keep all the shutters tightly closed.'

Jane shuddered. 'Ugh! How awful!'

'And that's about it. Now, let me see – ah, that's better.' She stood back a little to look at her handiwork, and Jane stared at her reflection, hardly daring to believe what she saw. Her normally straight hair was transformed, swept back and up, and skilfully pinned high on her head, a cascade of shiny soft curls sweeping down on to her neck. She moved her head slightly, experimentally, and laughed. 'That's *super*, Megan. You're a darling!'

'Just you sit still till I've sprayed you,' Megan said severely. 'There now. Go and slip on your dress, and we'll show your father.'

It was just an hour before the party was to start that Jane knew her father would not be going. She had slipped on her thin dressing gown and was painting her nails with colourless varnish when Ellen tapped on the bedroom door and came in.

'Your pa will skin mah hide off if he knows I'm here, but I've got to tell you, honey. He ain't fit to go out tonight, and that's the truth.'

Jane turned round in alarm, half rising from her seat. 'Ellen, what is it?'

Ellen put up a placating hand. 'Don't fret now. S'nothin' serious – but when he gets like this the best thing he can do is have an early night, and plenty of rest.'

'Oh, Ellen, of course. Then we won't go—'

'That's just it!' The housekeeper interrupted her, her plump face full of concern. 'He *knows* you'll feel like this, that's why he's insisting he's not going to spoil your very first night out, so he'll struggle along – and—' she shrugged, '—make himself real poorly.'

Jane nodded, beginning to understand the purpose now of the other's visit. 'If I say I'll go anyway, he won't mind, you mean?'

'That's it!' Ellen nodded in relief. 'It's all the excitement of you coming here that's done it. He'll be as right as rain in a day or two.'

'Then I'll go down and tell him now,' she paused on her way to the door. 'No, I can't do it. How can I go and leave him, Ellen?' Her face was filled with the concern she felt. 'I'd really rather not – I wouldn't enjoy it, knowing he wasn't well.'

Ellen heaved a huge sigh. 'You go down an' tell him now that you ain't goin' cos he's poorly – and you'll see him change his mind and tell you there ain't nothin' wrong with him. Your pa's a stubborn man, Miss Jane. I guess I tried,' she shook her head sadly, and turned to leave, her shoulders drooping. Jane caught her arm.

'All right, you win. I do understand, Ellen, I'd just hate him to think I wanted to go without him, that's all. But if it's for the best—'

'Oh, it is, honey, it is. 'Sides, you'll be goin' with Mr. Grant. Your pa knows he'll take good care of you.'

'Oh, no! I'd forgotten that!' Jane exclaimed, dismayed. Then, seeing the puzzled frown on the housekeeper's face, she added: 'I mean, shouldn't we let him know or something?'

'Bless you, honey, no! He'll be here in a little while. He'll be delighted to take you.' And with that, satisfied at the success of her little mission, she went out.

'Yes, he'll be delighted, I'm sure,' whispered Jane softly to herself. This was even worse. She put her hand to her face. Now, on top of everything else, she had the prospect of a journey with *that man* – just the two of them, and nothing to talk about, except, of course, she thought dryly, *her* selfishness in leaving her father. She went back listlessly to the mirror and regarded her expression sombrely. She wished that she were not going – but she had no choice now. Her face, paler than usual, stared back at her, her eyes large and luminous in the soft light from the lamp.

'Go on, feel sorry for yourself,' she told her reflection. 'You're doing fine.' And with those odd little words, there came a resolution. She rubbed her cheeks to restore her colour, and looked more defiantly at herself. Right! This was a challenge, she thought suddenly. Let's see how he behaves – and be ready for him. An unwilling smile curved her lips. He already thought the worst of her. The fact that she was going to the party and leaving her father at home would undoubtedly be another black mark against her in his opinion. What could happen to make the situation worse? Jane picked up her eyeshadow and began to make up her eyes. Megan had gone to a lot of trouble to do her hair nicely. The least she could do was to try and look her best. Slowly, carefully, quite unaware that she needed no artificial aids to enhance nature's own handiwork, Jane began to make up.

When she was satisfied that she looked reasonable – Aunt Dorothy had done her work well in undermining Jane's confidence – she put on the slippery silk dress, and after a struggle, managed to zip it up. Putting on her sandals, she checked that she had a handkerchief and comb in her bag, and picking up the fine silk stole, she went downstairs.

Jane faltered, her new-found confidence – born of defiance – deserting her momentarily when she heard voices from the sitting room. Surely Gavin hadn't arrived already? She bit her lip, standing still outside the closed door, filled with a sudden overwhelming panic. She couldn't go through with it – she *couldn't*. It was no use. She would have to—

The door was flung open, rudely interrupting her thoughts, and she gasped, her hand going to her breast.

Gavin appeared equally surprised. For a moment he stood perfectly still, then he moved back slightly. 'I'm sorry,' he said. His voice was cool, perfectly assured; he wasn't sorry at all. Jane looked at him, momentarily speechless, noting the casual perfection of the light fawn suit that he wore, with the gleaming white open-neck shirt setting off his dark tan, making him seem almost swarthy. His hair was brushed back, shiny as if still wet from a shower. Those deep grey eyes were watching her coolly. Jane took a deep breath, then swallowed. This was it! She was ready for him now.

'Thank you.' She gave him a little smile and sailed past him into the room and went over to her father.

'Ellen told me you're not well—' she began. He laid a tired hand on her arm and pulled her down beside him.

'Believe me, Ellen cannot be disobeyed! She's decided

I'm not fit to go out – and I lack the courage to defy her.'
He grinned at Gavin, standing nearby with a glass in his
hand. 'You know Ellen, Gavin. Tell Jane.'

Gavin shrugged, seeming for a moment almost amused.
'It's true. It would take a braver man than either of us to
disobey her.'

But he wasn't speaking to Jane, she knew that. His
amusement was for her father. In sudden panic she wondered how he would manage to ignore her all evening,
then gritted her teeth and forced a smile.

'I didn't want to go, Father, when she told me, but—'

'I insist! Gavin will look after you. I'd be most upset if
you tried to give up this party for me. Besides, an early
night will be all I need. Now—' he glanced at the slowly
ticking clock on the wall, 'best be off. It's a good way to
Sara's, and the road isn't the best in the world. Gavin
won't want to go fast, will you, eh?'

'You're right, John.' He put the glass down on a table.
'Is there anything you need before we go?'

Jane's father shook his head. 'Nothing, thanks. Ellen's
hovering about, waiting to shunt me off when you've
gone. Have a good time, Jane,' this as she stooped to kiss
him. 'You look absolutely lovely. I'm very proud of you,
my dear.'

'Thank you, Father.' Jane's eyes misted with tears at his
words, and she walked blindly to the door, aware that
Gavin was holding it open for her.

They went out to the front of the house to where his
white Mercedes stood, illuminated in the light flooding
out from the hallway.

In silence he opened her door, and Jane stepped in,
clutching her bag and stole. Her temples were throbbing
with sudden strain. Her door slammed, he strode round to
his own seat, and the next minute they were off.

CHAPTER FOUR

GAVIN drove swiftly down the drive. As they reached the gates, he said: 'Would you like the radio on?'

'Please,' Jane murmured, and the strains of a pop song filled the air. At least, she thought, it will save awkward gaps in the conversation – but perhaps there wouldn't be any conversation.

Her heart was thudding. It wasn't her imagination. Tension flowed around them in almost tangible waves, filling the car. He dislikes me, she thought. I know this already. Why can't I ignore it – but she knew that she couldn't. It was something that was beyond her power to cope with, unused as she was to men – especially men like him, assured, powerful, and wealthy, with the supreme confidence that wealth gives. She had no weapons to fight him, save the one she instinctively sensed – her femininity. Deep down inside her, she knew that in spite of his arrogance, she had the edge in something, a basic instinct that had survived since times primeval. Her very weakness, in fact, was her strength. It gave her a slight confidence. She sat back in the very comfortable seat and decided to let him do his worst.

'What time do these parties finish, Gavin?' she asked, after a few minutes' silence, filled with distant, foreign-sounding music.

'They go on all night sometimes. But you must tell me when you've had enough.'

Had enough! That sounded ominous! Almost as if he knew, as if he could read her mind. Damn the man for his insufferable arrogance, she thought coldly. If it's to be war, I'll be prepared now.

'It's your car,' she said politely. 'I'll leave that to you.'

'Will you?' His voice was smooth, disinterested, but she noticed that his hands gripped the wheel a little tighter. Her heart was filled with dismay. After midnight she knew she would want to go to bed. She determined there and then that come what may she would not ask him to take her home. Let him stay until the very end. She would not give him another excuse to find fault. Jane could imagine his face, almost hear his words, if she asked to leave while the party was in full swing. The resigned shrug, the implication that she was spoiling it for him. Oh, yes, she thought, you'd love that, wouldn't you?

'Of course,' she answered quickly. 'It's very kind of you to drive me there. You must decide when you wish to leave, and that will be fine by me.' She looked out of the window. They were going in the direction of Port Patrick, and everything was so different by night, magically transformed by the black velvety sky into a starry wonderland. Gavin had his window open, and a cool breeze filtered in and teased Jane's hair gently. She breathed deeply, already a little in love with the island and its mystery. If only it were Colin beside her, instead of Gavin! With him she would feel relaxed, basking in the warmth of unashamed admiration, instead of feeling guilty at taking this unwilling man's time up. The thought that Colin would be there with Megan was the one fact that cheered Jane. She might not even see Gavin at all, if the house was crowded. Almost childishly she crossed her fingers as if that might make the wish come true.

The tension in the car was dispelled somewhat as Jane relaxed. The music helped too; it gave her something to fasten her attention on. All her senses were alive to the man who sat only inches away, his sleeve brushing her arm slightly when he changed gear. Strength sat upon him lightly. His dark hawklike profile was busy on the road ahead when she risked a glance at him. He drove well, and there was no mistaking his skill at the wheel of the powerful motor. Trees and houses sped past in a grey-ish blur as they neared the town. Suddenly he swung left, into a smaller road, and they began a gradual climb. The moon was high above, flooding the island with cool yellow light, and she remembered that first night, when she had taken a fateful walk . . .

'How many more miles?' she asked.

'About fifteen,' was the casual reply. 'The road gets narrow soon, and I won't be able to go so fast.'

'Oh, I see.' They were alone in the darkness now. All houses had been left behind, and the road was a narrow ribbon of white unwinding before them. Jane glanced back to see, surprised, that they had climbed quite a lot. Distantly, moonlight gleamed on the dark waters of the Indian Ocean, and she said impulsively, forgetting just who she was with: 'Oh, how beautiful!'

Their eyes met briefly. 'Yes, it is.' Then she found the car slowing down, and he stopped. Panic flared inside her. Why on earth had he . . .

His brief laugh told her that he had read her thoughts. 'I thought you might like to get out and have a proper look. The view of the sea from here is quite something.'

'I – thank you.' Frightened to incur his wrath by re-fusing, Jane opened her door and stepped out behind the car. Then she heard his door open, and fought down that foolish sensation of fear that had assailed her. He was coming to look too, and that was all. He wasn't going to attack her, or anything like that. Her legs went weak, but she determinedly stood her ground, gazing far out at the magnificent panorama spread before them. He was beside her now. She moved slightly away, the desire to get back in the car inexplicably stronger than the wish to remain.

'I wasn't going to touch you,' he said, and strangely his voice had a harsh note, almost as if he had divined her thoughts. Something snapped inside Jane.

'I didn't imagine you were,' she retorted, a flare of anger making her voice sharp.

'No?' he was amused now – almost. 'You jumped as if you thought I was going to try and kiss you.'

'You must have imagined it,' she countered swiftly, surprised at her own temerity. She looked at him standing beside her, a mocking gleam on his dark face. 'I'm sure your manners are too impeccable for you to even think of such a thing. I certainly didn't.' She turned to go back to the car, saw the quick frown that crossed his features, and knew that somehow she had made him angry. Instead of dismaying her, as it should have done, it had the opposite effect.

She slid into the low-slung vehicle and shut her door firmly. Her heart hammered rapidly. Gavin joined her without a word, slammed his door, and set off swiftly and silently. And not another word was said on that journey.

The house was large and white, and ablaze with light. Jane's mood of defiance had evaporated, leaving her limp. As they sped up the drive, she sat up, her hands nervous on her bag. Swallowing hard, she stared at the cars lining the drive, some twenty or more. As they drew to a stop in front of a large imposing entrance, the door was flung wide open, and there standing on the step was a tall slim girl in a halo of golden light.

Gavin opened Jane's door, and the girl came down the steps.

'Gavin, *darling*!' she cried. 'Now the party can really begin.' Jane stood and watched, forgotten in the background as the girl – it could only be Sara – stood on tiptoe to kiss him.

'Hello, Sara,' he answered. 'Nice to see you. You look good enough to eat.'

Sara gave a low throaty chuckle, almost a purr, then held out her hand, as if remembering that he had someone with him.

'Hello, you must be Jane. How *lovely* of you to come,' she said, and their eyes met. Jane received a distinct shock. This girl was beautiful. Everything about her spoke of careful grooming, from her sleek blonde hair to the toes that peeped out from under a breathtakingly simple white dress that floated in filmy folds about her slender figure. Her eyes were large and dark, and they watched Jane in frank, skilful assessment as Sara said: 'How pretty you look. Do come in, I'm sure you want to freshen up after your journey.' She took Jane's arm firmly in her own, and called to Gavin over her shoulder: 'Find somewhere to park, lover. I'll look after Jane.'

Lover, she had said. Jane wondered if they were. She wouldn't be surprised. The affection with which he had greeted her was astonishing – for him. She had not thought him capable.

As they went through the wide hall towards the stairs, Jane said: 'I'm sorry my father wasn't able to come. He didn't feel well.'

Sara made a small polite sound. 'Oh, what a shame. Never mind, I'm sure you'll have a lovely time.'

She took Jane into a sumptuously furnished bedroom, and waved to the elegant dressing table laden with jars and bottles. 'Do help yourself, Jane,' she said. 'Come down when you're ready.' Then she stood and looked at her, and Jane could feel those beautiful eyes taking in every detail of her appearance. Sara suddenly smiled, as if satisfied at what she saw, then with another swift last look, went out. Jane sat shakily down. She closed her eyes for a moment. She wanted to run away and hide. Sara's behaviour, everything about her, had been calculated to make her feel gauche and young. And how well she had succeeded! Jane knew now what it felt like to enter a beauty contest. Sara's hard beautiful eyes had gone over her like a judge's at a competition, weighing up, adding points – and then dismissing her like some also-ran who wouldn't even get in the last fifteen. Jane was too naïve to realize just how clever Sara was at concealing her true feelings – and how she had shrewdly summed up Jane's innate shyness – and known how to take instant advantage of it.

With shaking hands Jane applied lipstick. She now knew exactly what Megan had meant. And how on earth would she get through the next few hours? Please, she prayed silently, please let Megan and Colin be downstairs. She took a deep breath and went to the door, listened for a moment to the babel of voices from downstairs, fought back the feeling of sheer panic and went quietly down the stairs, holding tightly to the exquisite wrought iron banister, hoping to creep in and find Megan before she was noticed . . .

'There you are!' Sara's voice was clear and loud. 'Look, everyone, here's Jane.' Sara had been waiting for her. As she approached the room, there was a sudden hush, as if everyone had been waiting too, and Jane saw a huge crowd of people, all talk and laughter suspended as they all watched her walk in with Sara beside her. Jane shook

75

— and then she saw a face amongst all those others, a sardonic, almost smiling face — Gavin. And she took a deep breath, as a voice nagged deep down inside her — wouldn't he just love it if you fell flat on your face! And something grew in Jane in that instant — a cold determination to show him. She smiled suddenly, and Sara said in her high clear voice:

'This is Jane, Augustus Ritchie's daughter. Jane, I'd like you to meet ...' She went through the names, and Jane found herself shaking hands with men and women, all of whom had drinks in their hands, all well dressed and elegant, and all weighing her up behind the smiles and conventional greetings that flowed round her. And she took it all in her stride, confidence miraculously returned because of a man's cynical grin. She didn't give a damn for him — or his friends.

Gradually the talk started again, and Jane was able to breathe freely, to relax, feeling the pressure recede as attention wandered to some newcomers. And Gavin had vanished into the crowd, and noise ...

Then Sara's mother was beside her. They had been introduced at the beginning, but Jane had barely been able to see her for the confusion. She could see what Sara would look like in twenty years. Leonie Smythe had her daughter's elegant patrician features, but her face was thinner, her cheekbones more prominent in her well-made-up face. And nothing could disguise the lines of discontent round her rather thin mouth. She handed Jane a glass, taken from a passing white-gloved waiter.

'I'm sure you need one, Jane,' she smiled, but it didn't reach her eyes, which were a cold hard blue, even more so than her daughter's.

'Thank you,' Jane accepted the glass. 'I don't drink, actually—'

'Heavens! It's only champagne. Very mild – it'll do you good, then we'll find you something even less potent later, if you insist. Drink up, dear.' She paused to wave to a man, then turned back to Jane. 'So you and Gavin came alone? A shame your father couldn't come, but there. Gavin's a sweetie, isn't he? He and Sara—' here she put a hand confidentially on Jane's arm '—are so much in love. They make a splendid couple, don't they?'

'Yes, they do,' agreed Jane fervently, knowing that her reasons would undoubtedly shock the other woman beyond measure.

'It won't be long now, I don't think, before we hear wedding bells,' she laughed girlishly, and then added in a whisper: 'But not a word to anyone. It's still a secret.'

'I won't say a word,' Jane promised. She sipped at the bubbly golden liquid in her glass, and it went down in an icy 'shoosh' into her stomach.

'Oh, do excuse me, I've just seen—' Mrs. Smythe's voice tailed away as she waved and yoohooed frantically to someone in the crowded noise-filled room, then darted off. Jane was left quite alone, suspended in a sea of laughing faces, isolated as surely as if she were on a desert island. Without pausing to think what she was doing, she lifted her glass and swallowed the champagne in one go. She gasped and blinked as the bubbles shot up her nose, and a dry Scots voice from beside her said: 'That's what I like to see – a good drinker.'

Jane hiccuped and turned, and looked into the smiling face of the middle-aged man who had come up quietly beside her. He was her own height, bald, with a sharp beaky nose and the most facinating eyes she had ever seen in a man, mesmeric, dark-lashed, and a startling shade of deep blue.

'You're Mac – I mean Dr. Macdonald,' she gasped,

recovering slightly from the effects of the drink.

'How did you guess that?' He lifted his own glass to her. 'Your good health, Jane.'

'Megan said you'd be here, and I couldn't miss that lovely accent,' she answered. 'But how did you know me?'

'Ah-hah,' he chuckled. 'You fit your description too – besides, I saw Sara give you the treatment.' He lowered his voice to a conspiratorial whisper. 'And Leonie. I was lurking behind that vase of flowers when she gave you the old spiel about Sara and Gavin.'

'You listened?' Jane's eyes widened.

'Aye! I'm a shady character – did you not know that? Megan's slipped up if she's no' told you.'

Jane laughed and shook her head, liking this man instinctively, and glad to have him to talk to. 'What did you mean about "the treatment?" ' she asked quietly.

'You don't know?' he raised one bushy eyebrow disbelievingly. 'Well, tell me, how did *you* feel walking into this room with her by your side shouting the odds, making everyone look at you?'

Jane pulled a little face. 'Awful,' she confessed.

'Aye,' he nodded. 'She's a little bitch right enough. Och, a beautiful one, I'll grant you, but a bitch for all that. Still, I must say you carried it off admirably.' He shook his head in wonder. 'Aye, you did that.'

'I did?' gasped Jane faintly. 'I was wishing myself a few thousand miles away from here.'

'The point is, my child, that you didn't show it. Now, see me?' he looked comically at her. 'Crowds terrify me – but you'd never think so to look at me, would you?'

'No, I wouldn't,' she laughed disbelievingly. 'You're only saying it to make me feel better, I know.'

'That I'm not,' he denied indignantly. 'Come away and

let's sit down in a quiet corner. I want a word with you about your dad.'

And so Jane found herself sitting beside this warm friendly man, and the party became brighter. The room grew crowded, and waiters circulated with drinks that vanished before they had walked a few feet. Gavin appeared, took a look at them, and vanished, swallowed up in the throng. And Jane and Mac talked and talked, oblivious of all this.

Then Megan appeared, greeted them both delightedly, and sat down.

'Colin's just parking the car. Heavens, what a crush!' she looked round her. 'We had a puncture, of all things, or we'd have been here ages ago. I did so want to be here when you arrived, Jane. Where's John?'

'He couldn't make it,' Jane answered. 'Ellen wouldn't let him come.'

'So you and Gavin came alone.'

'Yes, we did.' Megan looked briefly at Jane as she answered, seemed about to say something, then changed her mind. Instead she spoke to Mac. 'And what have you been telling Jane?'

Mac's face registered alarmed innocence. 'I've been a perfect gentleman, haven't I, Jane?'

Jane assured Megan that he had in fact been looking after her admirably, and then Mac went on to tell the older woman about Jane's entry into the party, accompanied by Sara.

Megan pulled a face. 'You don't need to tell me. That's why I was sorry we weren't here. Still, as Mac says, I'm sure you looked super, Jane. Now,' she looked around her. 'I could do with a drink.'

'Leave it to me.' Mac stood up. 'Save my seat,' he added before vanishing.

They heard music starting up in another part of the house, faintly, a vivid cacophony of sound, as of instruments being tuned, and Megan said: 'They'll be starting the dancing soon – then we'll have a buffet.'

Both looked up as Colin and Mac appeared, each carrying two glasses full of champagne. Colin greeted Jane as if delighted to see her, and she felt her heart lift. The one drink she had already had was taking effect, and she sensed that her cheeks were pink. Her head was delightfully light, almost as if filled with cotton wool, and she smiled back at him glowingly, aware of Megan's eyes upon her.

After that the party became a riot of colour, a whirling kaleidoscope of noise and pleasure after she sipped her second glass of champagne, and Colin took her firmly under his wing. They drifted off to the large patio at the rear of the house where the coloured group had begun to play. The patio led out on to the lawns, and couples were dancing on the brightly lit grass as well as on the stone-floored patio with its potted palms, and a small fountain tinkling prettily in the centre.

Colin held Jane tightly as he whirled her into a tango, steering skilfully among the other couples. She saw several people watching them, and wondered why, until he whispered: 'You're causing a sensation, Jane.'

She coloured instantly. 'Don't – don't make jokes,' she whispered back, stumbling slightly, a little hurt at his teasing. He held her tightly to steady her, his mouth only inches from her ear as he denied it. 'I'm not my sweet. Honestly, I wouldn't tease you, ever. You look so very beautiful, Jane.' His hand slid across her back as if to enclose her more firmly in his arms. 'Oh, but I want to kiss you. I'm not the only one either,' his eyes flickered over to a corner and as he whirled her round again,

Jane's eye was caught by that of a tall handsome man who, seeing her, raised his glass and smiled.

'That's Johnny Melia, a devoted admirer of *la belle* Sara's,' he grinned. 'Or perhaps I should say ex-admirer now. He's the biggest wolf on the island, so watch out if you dance with him.' He whirled deftly away from a couple gyrating silently in a corner, oblivious to everyone save themselves, and added softly: 'If you dance with him, stay where it's well lit. Don't say you've not been warned.'

'I thought Sara was—' Jane stopped abruptly.

'Was what?' he prompted.

'Was – well, aren't she and Gavin – er—'

He laughed. 'Who's been telling you *that*? Dear Leonie? Gavin's too wily a bird to be ensnared by Sara – until he wants to be. And so she keeps Johnny on ice just to keep Gavin on his toes.'

Jane was silent. She had seen the affection in Gavin's greeting. Colin hadn't.

The band was noisy, exuberant – and good. Several dances followed in quick succession, and in one she saw Gavin with Sara. They were holding each other tightly, apparently unaware of anyone else there. Sara's blonde head came nearly up to his shoulder, and Jane saw her eyes were closed as they drifted past in a dreamy waltz.

Suddenly she found herself going dizzy, and said to Colin: 'Can we sit this one out? The champagne's gone to my head.'

He drew her outside. 'Fresh air for you, sweetie,' he commanded firmly. In the cool air, away from the crowd, Jane shivered, and he put his arm round her. 'That better?' his voice was soft.

'Mmm, yes, I th-think so.' She turned a laughing face

up to him. 'I've never had champagne before, Colin.'

'Never?' he looked down at her in amused disbelief. 'Ah-huh! Very interesting! I must remember to ply you with lots, and then—' he twirled an imaginary moustache and leered, '— I shall have my wicked way with you.'

'Thanks for the warning,' she drew away in mock horror. 'I thought it was Johnny I had to watch, not you.'

Suddenly Colin pulled her close to him, and the expression on his face made her heart flip crazily. The next moment his lips came down on hers, sweet and warm and infinitely tender. Jane struggled instinctively, but only for a heartbeat of time before relaxing and yielding to that warmth.

Shakily he drew away and looked at her. 'Wow! I'm sorry, I shouldn't have—'

'Don't apologize,' she said quietly, then: 'H-hadn't we better go back in?'

'Frightened of me?' he teased.

Jane laughed. 'No, of course not.' She had wondered what it would be like, being kissed – and now she knew. In a way it was a disappointment. She had expected something wonderful, earth-shattering, and instead there was a sense of being let down. Enjoyable, but ... She couldn't understand why, for she liked Colin, and thought him pleasant and charming, but there was the oddest sense of anti-climax now that he had finally kissed her. Perhaps, she thought, as they went back into the dancing crowd, perhaps there's something wrong with me. The unaccustomed champagne was having its effect, and Jane, to her horror, discovered that she wanted to cry. Determined not to let it show, even for an instant, she threw herself wholeheartedly into the dancing.

She could not guess what a stunning figure she made,

tall and slender in her beautiful dress, her hair shiny and slightly awry, her skin glowing with health as she laughed and danced the evening away.

Once, as she was dancing with Johnny Melia, she turned to see Gavin standing alone, apart from the crowd, smoking a black cheroot. His gaze was hard and dark upon her, and for a moment their eyes met and held in a strange unblinking clash. Defiantly she smiled at Johnny as if he were the nicest person there, and felt a small stab of satisfaction at seeing Gavin turn quickly away and walk outside into the darkness. The moment was forgotten as Colin whirled past with an attractive girl, and winked at her.

The food that she ate soon afterwards helped to sober Jane somewhat. A long buffet table was set out in the dining-room, and she went in with Colin, Megan and Mac to join the scramble for the beautifully set out supper. As they moved along, holding their plates and forking up morsels of chicken and ham and dozens of other delightful portions of exotic food, she heard a voice say: 'Are you enjoying yourselves?' and looked round to see Gavin standing by them. 'Hello, stranger,' Megan greeted him. 'We haven't seen much of you.'

'No?' he smiled slightly, his teeth very white against that dark tan. 'I've been circulating. It is rather crowded, though.' He turned to Jane, who stood with Colin. 'And you, Jane. Is the party coming up to expectations?'

'Yes, thank you,' she answered politely. 'Is it for you?'

He nodded. 'As much as any party can,' and his voice, she noted, was cool. Perhaps the drink had made her reckless, or perhaps it was the sudden flash of memory, seeing his face watching her when she had first entered the room with Sara. Whatever the cause, she didn't know what made her say next: 'Then just tell me when *you've* had enough, and we'll go.' And she turned her back on him and determinedly speared a large slice of chicken. There was a moment of pregnant silence, then he answered: 'I will. If you'll excuse me?' And then he was gone towards Sara, who had just come into the room with her mother. Jane didn't see Megan's amused glance towards Mac, but she heard Colin breathe: 'What was that in aid of?'

She turned towards him, her eyes sparkling with defiance. 'Was I rude?'

Colin pulled a wry face. 'Let's say people don't usually talk to Gavin in that way.'

'More's the pity,' Jane said, feeling, however, a twinge of dismay. She had no intention of telling Colin why she had said what she had. Clearly Gavin could do no wrong in his eyes. She heard Megan chuckle, and looked around.

'Good for you, Jane,' she said very quietly, so that not even Colin could hear. Jane let out her breath in a sigh. One person was on her side anyway. She was already regretting the reckless impulse that had made her answer Gavin so. She was not usually rude to anyone – but then Gavin wasn't the usual sort of person. And Jane had a horrible feeling inside her, deep down, that he would not forgive her for what she had said. It would, she realized resignedly, have to go on his ever-growing list of her faults.

She felt a little better after supper. Sara came over to them, smiling sweetly, her eyelashes fluttering coyly at the two men.

'I do hope you're all enjoying yourselves,' she said, and Jane noted without surprise that she had a slight lisp. It made her appear gently feminine, and Colin and Mac

84

seemed to like it as they both assured her that they were indeed. Everything, in fact, was superb.

'I'm so glad,' she said, with a sweet look at Megan and Jane. Her clear fair skin was only faintly tanned, and her dark eyes were luminous.

'It's so lovely having you, Jane,' she put out her hand to rest it on Jane's arm. 'I hope you'll come often while you're staying here. And perhaps we can have a day out in Port Patrick some time?'

'Yes, that would be nice,' agreed Jane, wondering why the other girl was being so nice to her.

'Good. I'll phone you in a day or two. Do excuse me now, one of the waiters seems to be having a little trouble.' She glided away, and Mac sighed. 'My, my,' he murmured. 'You're honoured. Still, I dare say she has her reasons – like keeping a friendly eye on you to make sure you don't pinch her boy-friend.' Megan and Jane looked at one another, and wouldn't tell Mac why they began to laugh.

It was much later that Jane began to feel tired, almost ill. She knew that it was due to the champagne, which she had foolishly continued to drink. Everyone had assured her that it was the mildest possible drink for *anyone*, but now she began to doubt it. Her head was muzzy, and every step she took was like treading on bouncy cotton wool. And she knew she must not – dare not – ask Gavin to take her home, for what would he say then? She and Megan were sitting in a comparatively quiet corner on their own for a few minutes, and Jane looked round in desperation. She could feel perspiration beading her brow.

'I'm going to the bathroom,' she whispered.

'Are you all right?' Megan asked, her voice full of concern.

'Fine,' Jane lied. 'Just a little tired – I'm not used to late nights, that's all. I won't be long.'

'I'll come with you—' Megan began, and Jane shook her head, then winced, wishing she hadn't. 'No, honestly, I'll be all right.' She needed to be alone, above all.

No one noticed her slipping upstairs. She bathed her face and hands in the bathroom, and sat quietly for a few moments, then set off down the lushly carpeted corridor, which was waving most alarmingly up and down, like the deck of a ship in a storm. Jane passed an open bedroom door, saw the neatly made bed, and, succumbing to an overwhelming temptation, went unsteadily in, kicked off her sandals, and with a little sigh of relief, lay down. 'Just five minutes,' she murmured to herself. That was all she needed to put her right again, she knew.

A hand was shaking her, and a voice was saying, from a great distance: 'Jane, are you all right?'

Struggling through mists of sleep, Jane opened her eyes to see the wavering outline of a man illumined in the light from the open door. Horrified, she struggled to sit up, and her head swam alarmingly, then cleared sufficiently for her to see that it was Colin standing there.

'C-Colin! I fell asleep – how – how long have I b-been here?'

He laughed and sat down beside her on the bed. 'It's all right, don't panic. Only about a quarter of an hour. Mum told me you'd gone a bit peaky, so I guessed you might have sneaked a little lie-down. She was just coming to look for you, but I volunteered. Are you feeling ill?'

Jane struggled into a more comfortable position, assisted by him. 'No. I was so tired – and my head was going round. I'm sorry.'

'I've told you not to worry. Look, do you want me to

drive you home? It's nearly two anyway.'

'Will you?' her eyes widened hopefully. 'I'm supposed to be going with Gavin, but he wants to stay till the end, I'm sure, and all I want to do is go to bed.' She gave a little laugh. 'I'm not used to parties – or champagne.'

'I know.' His arms were still around her, warm and infinitely reassuring. 'Look, I'll go down and tell Gavin you're coming with me, and—' He stopped abruptly as a shadow fell across the floor in that darkened room, followed by Gavin himself. There was a short silence as he looked at Jane and Colin, his face quite expressionless. Then, slowly, he said: 'Excuse me. I wouldn't have come in, but I thought I heard someone call me.'

Jane felt her face flame in the merciful darkness. The lightness of his tone didn't hide the subtle contempt expressed in his words. Colin took his arms away from Jane. 'I was just coming down to see you, Gavin,' he began. 'I've just told Jane I'll take her home.'

'Do you want to leave now, Jane?' Gavin asked.

'Yes.'

'Then *I'll* take you.' His voice had a ring of finality about it.

'But—' she began, followed by Colin's:

'It's all right—'

Colin might not have been there. Even in the dark room, with Gavin's face partly shadowed, she knew that his eyes were on her, filled with something that she didn't understand as he said: 'I brought you. I promised your father I'd take you home.'

She waited for Colin to sort it out, to make everything all right – but he didn't. He shrugged, looked at Jane as if to say, 'It's no use arguing,' and said: 'Okay, Gavin, you're the boss.'

There was a sudden, electric silence. Gavin turned

round and went out. Quietly he said, as he went: 'I'll have the car at the front door in five minutes. Meanwhile, I'll go and make our apologies to our hostesses.'

They heard his footsteps faintly along the thick carpet, and Colin let out his breath in a deep relieved sigh. 'God, but he's good and mad,' he said.

Jane sat up and clutched him as if he were a lifebelt. 'Why didn't you insist—' she began, a tremor of fear running through her.

'You heard the man. He promised your father *he'd* take you home. That's it, with Gavin. No argument, no discussion. Believe me, I *know* him. You don't, my sweet.'

He stood up and assisted Jane to her feet. 'Leonie will be pleased – and so will dear Sara.' He suddenly began to smile. 'I'm looking forward to seeing her face after you two have gone. Her golden boy's never left before the party's over before.'

Jane's heart sank dismally. She had done what she vowed she wouldn't – dragged Gavin away before he wanted to go. She picked up her bag and went down the stairs with Colin, feeling utterly wretched. There was no one about, but loud voices and laughter, and the chink of glasses, came distantly from the patio. Thankfully she slipped out of the door, and said:

'Explain to your mother and Mac, won't you, please?'

Colin nodded and stepped back, and Jane turned and walked down the steps, feeling as if she were going to her execution.

CHAPTER FIVE

THE car was waiting. Gavin stood by the door, holding it open for her. Jane waved to Colin, then got in, feeling as if her last link with civilization was severed as she heard the front door to the house shut. Gavin closed her door quietly, walked round the front and slid into his driver's seat. He glanced briefly at her.

'Comfortable?' he said.

'Yes, thank you.' She couldn't have put into words just how wretched she felt, or how his icy cold anger dismayed her. She sat rigidly in the seat, not daring to relax in case she disgraced herself by falling asleep. The prospect of an hour's journey with this grim-faced man was daunting beyond words. He began to drive swiftly away from the house, and Jane watched it recede as they sped into the blackness, flinging ghostly grey shapes of trees into sharp relief, and casting dark shadows as the Mercedes purred swiftly and powerfully through the night.

Gavin jabbed a finger to push the cigar lighter in, and asked briefly: 'Do you object to me smoking?'

'No, no, of course not.' As if, she thought wildly, she would dare object! Nobody argued with Gavin – not even Colin. She couldn't analyse her sick feeling of disappointment at the way Colin had immediately acquiesced to Gavin in the bedroom. How she wished that she had never gone there! How too, she now wished that she had never spoken so sharply in the dining-room!

She watched the lighter glow, heard the click as it switched off, and he reached out and lit the black cheroot between his lips.

The faint aromatic scent of tobacco filled the car, and Jane looked out of the side window, praying that she wouldn't feel sick. Her head ached with a slow steady throb of pain and her eyes seemed filled with sand. Unable to bear the heavy silence any longer, she burst out: 'I'm sorry I dragged you away from the party.'

'Are you?' The cigar glowed redly as he turned his head to look at her.

'Yes.' She swallowed hard. 'That's why I wanted to come with Colin—'

'And you'd have let him take you home?'

She turned startled eyes towards him. 'Of course. I knew you'd want to stay until the end—'

'I told you to let *me* know when you wanted to leave. When I undertake to do something, I do it. I told your father that I would bring you safely home, and I will do just that, regardless of what time it is.'

She felt as if she were fighting an implacable force. Desperately she answered: 'He would have understood.'

'That's not the point, is it?' Contempt lashed her icily. Some spark of defiance, born of her sheer wretchedness, flared in Jane.

'It must be nice to be perfect,' she ground out bitterly. 'To always do the *right thing*.'

He flicked ash carefully into the ashtray and laughed. 'Let's not descend to personal insults.' There was no humour in the laugh. Jane clenched her hands, filled with an intense, frightening anger. His eyes flickered to her lap, seeing the tense grip on her knees, noting her quickened breathing. In a completely impersonal tone he continued: 'I'd try and relax if I were you. We have a long journey ahead of us.'

'How can I relax with *you*?' she answered. 'You make

it quite clear how much you resent your task. Oh, you don't need to say it – I can feel it.' She put a hand to her aching forehead, pressing hard to stop it from bursting.

He put his foot down on the brakes, and the car glided to a stop. Switching off the engine, he turned to her. 'Right, get it off your chest. I'm listening. What exactly do you mean?'

Jane looked round. There was no light, no sound anywhere. They were alone in a vast desert of blackness, just the two of them, isolated in the small area surrounded by the vehicle, and now she knew why Colin had given in so readily. The man's power was frightening. He waited for her to speak, the cigar end glowing steadily in that blackness, a waiting tiger, ready to pounce.

She had no weapons to fight him, nothing at all. And because she knew she could not win in this battle of wills, because nobody ever won against Gavin, she dredged an odd kind of courage from the depths of her being to enable her to say: 'All right, I'll tell you. You make it quite clear how much you resent me. I d-don't know why – I've done nothing to you. You should learn to judge people by what they *are*, not what you imagine them to be,' as she spoke, her voice grew stronger and less hesitant. She had nothing to lose, she knew that now. And the worst he could do would be to turn her out and make her walk – and that prospect was quite appealing compared to riding with him. She even turned round and touched the door handle, as if considering the idea. He saw the movement and said sharply: 'Where are you going?'

'Nowhere – yet. I was thinking it would be preferable to walk home than to ride with you.'

'Did you? You'd find your mistake after a few dozen yards. Unless you like bats in your hair, of course?' His voice held amused scorn. Jane, unable to help herself, snapped:

'I'm not frightened of them, if that's what you mean. They're only flying mice – they're more frightened of humans than we are of them.'

'You surprise me. Most women would faint at the thought.' He stubbed out his cigar in the ashtray.

'I'm not "most women". Although why you should think we're any more lacking in courage than men I don't know.' Jane was vaguely aware that the conversation was veering fast away from its original subject, but she couldn't do anything about it. She had to go on: 'Women aren't stupid, helpless creatures any more – or has nobody told you? We've even got *brains*, believe it or not.'

'All right. You made your point.' He jabbed at the cigar lighter again, and Jane said: 'Do you need a *cigar* to give *you* courage?' She was appalled at her own words, but something was driving her on, a force that she didn't understand, only that she somehow wanted to get under *his* skin, to prick his invulnerability and see what lay underneath. In the dim light from the dash, she saw the muscles tighten in his cheek, heard his indrawn breath, and knew, with dizzy apprehension, that she had scored, however lightly.

'No, I don't,' he spoke calmly, his temper on a tight leash, and it was more unnerving than hearing the scorn. The quiet voice went on: 'But a cigar is a pleasant antidote to childish behaviour.'

'I'm not ch-childish,' she stammered.

'You surprise me. You've given a very good impression of it so far. Now, have you finished? Can we continue our journey?'

'I don't know why you stopped. You're *hateful!*' she gasped.

'Don't push your luck too far – *Miss* Ritchie,' he made

her name sound vaguely insulting, 'my patience is wearing very thin.'

Slowly and deliberately he lit another cheroot, and pushed the lighter back into place with a slight click. The aromatic scent of the newly lit cigar was the last straw. With a faint sigh that was more like a moan, Jane pushed open the door and dashed out to the shelter of the welcoming palms, and was sick.

Shaken and trembling, she stood at last, her legs like jelly beneath her. She dimly heard a car door slam, and in her confused state thought he was about to drive off. She felt too ill to care, and waited for the sound of the engine to fill the air. Instead there were quick footsteps, and then his voice: 'What's the matter? Are you ill?'

Stumblingly she turned, felt her legs buckle beneath her as the ground swayed and trembled. The next second she was swung upwards in Gavin's arms, and he was carrying her to the car.

'Put me down – leave me—' she managed to gasp, struggling vainly against unreasoning panic.

He pushed her into her seat. 'Sit still,' he commanded, and strode round to his own side. The next moment he was beside her, the interior light flooded on, and she found a clean white handkerchief being pushed into her hands. 'Hold that.'

He reached into the glove compartment and lifted out a bottle. Opening it, he sprinkled some of the liquid on to the handkerchief, filling the car with a fresh tangy perfume.

'Now, wipe your face with that,' he said. 'It will help.'

Jane did so with trembling hands, the sharp coldness shocking her back almost to normal.

'Thank you,' she managed to whisper. It was as if a

truce had been called. He was impersonal, efficient, his tone no longer angry.

'Why didn't you tell me you were ill?' he asked, watching her.

She looked back into that lean face so near her own. 'I – I thought you knew,' she whispered. 'That's why I went to lie down.'

He made a quick impatient gesture. 'How could I know? I thought you'd gone up for a – a—' it was his turn to hesitate, and Jane's face went hot.

'What did you think?' she asked, horrified.

'I thought you'd gone for a necking session—' at her involuntary gasp, he added: 'I apologize. I realize now that I was wrong, but for God's sake why didn't you or Colin tell me?'

Jane turned her head away, tears welling out and spilling down her cheeks. A small sob escaped her. She was overwhelmed by all that was happening, and felt very lost and hurt.

'It doesn't matter,' she managed at last, her voice still shaky. 'Please go now. I'm better.'

'Not while you're crying.'

'I'm not c-crying,' she denied, brushing furtively at her cheeks.

'No? It sounds remarkably like it to me. For heaven's sake try and stop. I've apologized. What would you have thought in my place?' She shook her head wordlessly. What did it matter anyway? Why should she be so concerned about *his* opinion?

Carefully she wiped her face with the handkerchief, and when she had finished, put it in her bag. 'I'll wash it and return it,' she said, in a more normal tone. 'I'd like to go now, please. I'm very tired.'

Their eyes met, and in the dim light she seemed to see

something in his face that turned her body to fire. Just for an instant, but tension filled the air, as, mesmerized, she stared into his eyes, dark and shadowed in that small pool of light. She heard him breathing, saw the rise and fall of his chest, the dark shadowed hollow at his neck, the strong column of his throat, and his face, lean and dark, infinitely virile. A hard face, with a mouth that could be cruel and hard, or, as it was now, seeming almost to curve sensually. And Jane had the most awful urge to reach out and touch his lips with her fingertips, and they tingled as if the thought had become the deed. She pressed her hands together, willing herself to normality, and he spoke softly:

'Why on earth did you let yourself get in that state? I remember you told me you didn't drink.'

'I don't. They – I thought champagne wasn't s-strong,' she answered.

He gave a disbelieving laugh. 'Strong? I suppose it's not – if you're used to it. But you – didn't you *know*?'

'How could I?' she answered simply. 'I've never tried it before. I won't make the same mistake again,' she added.

'Then perhaps it's a timely lesson.' He switched on the engine, and the car burst into throbbing life. 'Are you ready now?'

'Yes,' she nodded.

'Then put your head back and try to rest. I won't go fast.'

She did so, feeling strangely calm, and the car moved slowly forward, increasing speed every second as he drove carefully down the road.

Jane closed her eyes and tried vainly to sleep. At least she didn't have to talk to him. But she could think, and that was worse in a way, for the thoughts that jostled in her head were oddly disturbing, and she kept seeing his mocking face looking at her across a room. And vaguely too came the realization that he had never answered her when she had challenged him about his resentment of her. Somehow, subtly, in a way that she was too tired to remember now, the subject had been changed.

Gavin stopped at the gates of her father's house, and switched off.

'We'll walk up the drive,' he said. 'Where's your key?'

'In my bag.' Jane opened it and began searching for the key that Ellen had pressed into her hand just before she left. She looked through quickly, then frowned, and began feeling more thoroughly in every corner. Gavin drew in his breath sharply. 'You *have* got one?'

'Yes. Ellen gave me one and I put it in my bag straight away.' With a quick despairing gesture she tipped the bag upside down on her knee and began to riffle through the contents. A lipstick, mirror, comb, two hankies – one Gavin's – small scent stick, but no key.

'May I?' He took the empty bag from Jane and put his hand in, feeling along the lining. Then he swore softly, almost inaudibly.

'It's not here now. Did you drop your bag at any time?'

'No—' she began, then remembered. 'When I went up to lie down – it fell on the floor with my stole – oh! I've forgotten that—'

'Never mind the stole.' He handed her back the empty bag and she began to put everything back. 'Did it fall open?'

'I d-don't know. Colin picked it up – I – it must have done.'

Without another word he got out, closed his door, and came round to hers. 'Come on, we'll try and get in. Quietly now.'

Jane didn't need telling. She had no intention of doing anything to make him more impatient than he already was. She ran after him as he strode along the curving path to the house, and she crossed her fingers tightly, hoping that a downstairs window would be open. This nightmare evening was one she would never forget, she thought miserably as she stumbled in her high-heeled sandals, trying to keep up with Gavin's long strides.

The house was dark and sleeping as they neared it. Gavin made a gesture of silence, and tried the front door first, then began walking along testing the windows. They stared blankly back at him, but nothing moved, and when he vanished round the back she waited, hardly daring to breathe. He returned in less than a minute. His face told her the answer without her needing to ask.

He came up close and looked down at her for a moment, his face inscrutable. 'What we can do now is try and wake Ellen,' he said. 'But we'll almost certainly rouse your father as well – and I don't want to do that. There's only one other alternative.'

'Yes?' Her eyes were large as she stared at him in dawning realization.

'And that is to sleep at my home.' As he spoke he was walking away from the house, his arm on hers, drawing her away, so that they could speak more freely. She stiffened and stopped walking, jerking her arm free.

'Oh no,' she said. 'Oh, no!'

His mouth tightened. 'Right. What do you suggest?' he asked softly.

'Couldn't we throw a pebble at her window?'

'Which is her room?'

'I – I don't know. It's at the back of the house some-where—' her voice trailed off miserably.

'If you think I'm standing here heaving rocks up at various windows, you're mistaken,' he retorted. 'There's no guarantee she'd waken then. I should imagine she sleeps like a log. Don't forget she goes to bed late and gets up early. Come on.' He took her arm again, less gently, and they reached the car in tense silence.

Jane turned to him. 'The garage isn't locked,' she said. 'I can sleep in the car—'

'Don't be a little fool,' he said roughly. 'Get in.' And he opened her door impatiently.

Two minutes later they were outside his house, where a light burned in the hall, flooding out over the drive. Gavin ran up the steps and put his key in the lock, turning round impatiently as Jane didn't move from the car.

'Come in,' he commanded, and she, so unhappy that she could scarcely bear it, obeyed. She blinked at the overhead light, then froze as the huge dog bounded towards his master, stumpy tail wagging furiously as he jumped up at a now smiling Gavin.

'All right, boy. Down!' He turned to Jane. 'He won't touch you – don't be afraid.'

She looked at them both, at the huge Dobermann on his hind legs trying to lick Gavin's face, and answered: 'I'm not frightened of dogs – except perhaps when they leap out at me from the dark.'

'Then you'd better say hello to him. Carlo, sit for Jane.'

The dog obediently heaved himself down and walked over to her, his lean intelligent face politely question-ing.

'Hello, Carlo.' Jane held out her hand for him to sniff, and the dog sat in front of her, his short stump of tail wagging furiously. He whined, and she stroked his head, smiling at the soft brown eyes reassuring her that he wouldn't bite.

'Why, you're beautiful,' she said softly, and knelt to stroke him. 'And you're not fierce at all, are you?'

He whined again, and licked her hand. Jane looked up, and Gavin was standing there with the strangest, most heart-stopping expression on his face, just watching her . . .

It made Jane so uneasy that she stood up quickly, her heart starting to hammer. She had never seen his face quite like that before . . .

'I'll make coffee. We'll have it in the kitchen,' he turned away abruptly, and after a moment's hesitation, she followed. The whole situation was beginning to take on a dreamlike quality, with such an air of unreality that Jane found herself wondering what more could possibly happen. The dog followed her to the kitchen, and she waited by the door until Gavin said: 'Sit down. I'll get you a couple of aspirins in a minute. You won't have such a hangover in the morning if you take them with your coffee. Are you hungry?'

'No, thanks,' she shook her head. Could this *really* be happening? Was she actually in that man's house, about to drink his coffee – and to sleep in one of his beds? At that thought she looked hastily down to the bag on her knee. Swallowing hard, she asked, scarcely daring to look at him: 'Er – I hope we won't wake your housekeeper?'

He turned the kettle off before answering, then he looked round at her. 'What you really mean is – is there anyone else in the house?'

Jane's face tightened at his bluntness. She took a deep breath. 'All right, I suppose I did.'

'Then I'm sorry to tell you that we're alone. My housekeeper and her husband live in a bungalow in the grounds.' He set a cup of black coffee in front of her, and put milk and sugar beside them. 'But you needn't worry. I don't seduce children!'

Jane gasped, her face flaming into colour. 'I didn't mean – oh!' she stammered, hating him.

'Yes, you did.' He opened a drawer and took out a small bottle, and put it before her, and then pulled up a chair to sit at the opposite side of the table. There was a glint that might almost have been amusement in his eyes as he went on: 'Don't look so furious. It's perfectly natural to wonder. I've just told you, so now you can forget it.' He tapped the bottle. 'Take two of those and drink your coffee. It's past three, and you're not the only one who's tired.'

Jane's thoughts were utterly confused, her mind a turmoil of mixed emotions. She opened the bottle and took out two of the small white pills. He really was utterly loathsome! With hands that shook, she drank the hot sweet drink, gasping a little as it went down into her empty stomach. How could he be so brutal, so – so – her mind searched for words with which to describe him, but failed. She realized just how desperately tired she was in fact, and bent to stroke the patient animal sitting by her side.

Gavin stood up. 'Come, Carlo. Out.' He went and opened the door, letting in the cool scented night air, and the dog obediently ran out. He looked at Jane then. 'I'll show you to your room.'

She swallowed the last of the coffee and stood up, then had to grip the table as the room swung round. Gavin frowned. 'You're not still feeling ill, are you?'

'No,' she shook her head. 'Just tired.' She flinched as he came towards her, and he smiled grimly. 'I'm going to show you your room, that's all.'

He led her back through the hall, and they went up-stairs. Everything was quietly luxurious, the light gleaming and reflecting off gold-framed mirrors and high wide windows. On the landing he touched Jane's arm lightly. 'This way.'

He led her into a small, beautifully furnished room with a snowy white cotton coverlet over the bed, and white rugs on the polished floor.

Flicking on the light, he pointed to a door. 'You have your own bathroom through there. There are tooth-brushes, soap, towels – everything you'll need. And you'll find an assortment of nightclothes in the top drawer of the dressing-table. I'm going to let Carlo in and lock up. If you want anything, you have only to ask.' He walked back to the door, and then paused, looking at Jane as she stood on a white fluffy rug by the bed. 'There isn't a lock on the door, I'm afraid. But you have my word that you won't be disturbed in any way.' His dark grey eyes met hers in a cool level glance, almost as if challenging her to say anything.

'Thank you,' was all she could manage. He went out, closing the door softly behind him, and Jane let out her breath in a long shuddering sigh. She sat on the bed to try and collect her scattered thoughts. He was proving unpredictably puzzling and disturbing. Could this be the same man she had seen laying down the law, 'causing a scene' at the airport? And what would Aunt Dorothy think about her present predicament? She dared not even contemplate. Standing, Jane went into the bathroom, softly and beautifully decorated with cool blue tiles from ceiling to floor, and plants on a stand against the wall. A thick fluffy blue towel waited to be used, as did the big bar of soap, the new toothbrush still in a slip of plastic, and some talcum powder. Jane rinsed her face and hands, and cleaned her teeth, feeling much better immediately. Then she went back into the bedroom and opened the top drawer of the dressing-table. Neatly folded flat were several nighties, and two pairs of pyjamas. She lifted out the top, nearest nightie, a thin cotton garment with pink flowers embroidered at the neck and on the gathered sleeves. Closing the drawer and flinging the nightie on the bed, Jane then loosed her hair from the confining pins and shook it free with a sigh of relief. She put up her hands to undo the zip of her dress, and pulled. Nothing happened. She tugged more firmly, then winced as a strand of hair became enmeshed in the fine teeth of the zip. 'Damn, damn!' she muttered, as her arms became rapidly tired of this vain exercise. Pausing for breath, she then tried again. But nothing budged, and now she felt her hair being pulled every time she tried to move her head. She felt an unreasoning panic. What on earth would she do now?

Jane tried to ease the dress up and over her head, but it was too slim-fitting round the waist, and after a few moments of grim silent struggle, in which she feared to tear the delicate material, she gave up. She looked at the door. There was only one thing to do – she would have to ask Gavin. Quickly, knowing she had no choice, and before her tired resolve failed, Jane opened the door and looked towards the stairs. He would probably still be down in the kitchen – and that thought was somehow cheering. It might not seem so bad, asking him for help, in that brightly lit room, instead of a bedroom.

Jane went quietly down, along the hall to the kitchen, and after a momentary pause to pluck up her waning courage, she pushed open the door and went in.

It was empty, and the back door was wide open. A

sudden feeling of panic assailed her. Everything was so quiet, as if he and Carlo had vanished. She went to the open door and stepped out, not daring to call him, prepared to wait. The next moment Carlo trotted up with a small 'woof' of pleasure, and she leaned down to stroke him.

'Where's your master?' she asked, and the dog pricked his ears and whined softly. Jane stepped out of the circle of light from the door, and listened. Distantly came the sound of the sea, a soft muted murmur that hinted of mystery, and the unknown creatures living in those cold green depths. She shivered, suddenly cold, and saw in the distance, a man coming towards her. Instinctively she moved forward. The sooner she asked, the better, and if the kindly darkness masked her foolishness, it wouldn't be so bad.

'Jane? What is it?' He strode up to her, and Carlo greeted him with delight.

'I can't undo the zip on this dress,' she burst out.

'And you want me to do it?' Even without seeing his face, for it was dark, and velvet shadows hid his features, she sensed his exasperation – and something else, indefinable. 'You're taking a chance, aren't you?' The dry mockery was there too.

'I b-bought it from your store,' she answered, wondering why she felt weak. 'It's not my fault.' It was the best she could think of.

'Come into the light.'

'No. Here.' She was full of panic again, and didn't know why, only that he mustn't see her face.

'You silly child!' He reached up and took hold of her hair to move it forward, and his hand brushed her neck, sending a shiver down her spine. It was like a sudden electric shock, and Jane took a deep breath and turned slightly away. She felt Gavin's long fingers on the neck of her dress, at the back, and her heart was hammering wildly, so that she feared he would hear. She stood perfectly still, unable to move even had she wished, heard his muttered exclamation: 'How the hell do you expect me to see in the dark?' but his words barely registered, such strange things were happening inside her. Butterflies of apprehension fluttered alarmingly in her stomach. His fingers were warm, touching her neck, and she felt his warm breath as he said softly: 'Ah, I think that's done. There was some—' he stopped abruptly, because a strange thing had happened. There came a dry leathery beat of wings just above their heads, a frightened squeak as a dark shape brushed upwards past them, and Jane turned and clutched wildly at Gavin in sudden fright.

'It was only a bat, you idiot child. Remember, they're more frightened of—' and then he stopped, and his arms, which had been about to move down to his side, from her neck, instead went round her. Their faces were a mere whisper away from each other, and his eyes were dark pools of shadow, hers wide with fear – and something else, something she didn't understand. Silence stretched to infinity, and Jane's heart went on dizzily beating, and her whole being was suffused with a strange sensation she had never imagined before. The shadows melted and fused, and blended together as Gavin's mouth came down on hers in a kiss that was like nothing that had ever happened to her before. Wordlessly they clung together, and he lifted his hand, to run it through her hair so that he could hold her even more closely.

And then, suddenly, and with a cruel abruptness that was startling, he pulled himself away, and in a voice that shook, said: 'My God, you don't know what you're doing!' And as Jane stood there, trembling with reaction, and still unable to move, there came to her a sudden memory – painful, still cruelly sharp after several years – a memory of her aunt, and of something that had happened, and that had been in a way strangely like this. She had rushed home from school one day full of happiness, bursting to tell Aunt Dorothy the good news – that she had won a prize for her drawings. She had flung her arms round the older woman, to hug her – and Aunt Dorothy had pushed her away, her mouth tightening in an all too familiar way as she exclaimed: 'What on earth do you think you're doing?'

Jane, rejected, hurt beyond words, had gone out of the room to cry alone in her bedroom. And this – *this* was history repeating itself. Just so did she feel now. That all too familiar pain filled her breast, rising to her throat to nearly choke her, and she turned away with a cry and ran towards the house.

She heard his footsteps coming after her, and flung out her arm with a cry, as if to ward him off, as he cried: 'Jane – wait!'

'Leave me – keep away!' Her body cringed from any further humiliation as she stumbled into the kitchen with its hard clear light beating down mercilessly on her.

'Wait!' A hard muscular hand clamped down on her arm, and she found herself being twisted round, her hair falling in wild disarray over her face as she twisted desperately, trying to free herself from that grip of steel.

'Don't touch me – don't—' What madness had possessed her, to allow her to have responded to this man's exciting touch as she had? And all that was left were the bitter ashes of humiliation and self-disgust as she beat vainly at his chest with her free hand. She kept her head turned away to escape the mockery she knew she would see in his eyes. She would not be able to bear *that*. She should have known – for were they not two of a kind, her aunt and him? It was no use. He was so much stronger than her, and with a little sigh, she went limp, unable to fight him any longer.

'Look at me, Jane,' his voice was a whiplash of steel. As if urged by a force greater than she could resist, she looked up, eyes wet with tears, her long silky lashes dark with them. She swallowed, her throat aching with an ache that nothing would appease. He could not humiliate her further now, at least. And she waited for his words. His eyes had gone very dark. There was none of the mockery she had feared, but something else instead. 'I'm sorry, Jane,' he said.

She wrenched her arm free from his grasp, and stepped backwards.

'Sorry!' she gasped. 'I'm sure you are – why don't you laugh? I'm sure you must be laughing inside. No—' as he moved slightly, 'keep away from me. I hate you, do you hear me? I hate you!' Then, horrified, hand to mouth, she ran from the room.

CHAPTER SIX

SHE thought she would never sleep. Her body burned like fire as she lay between the cool sheets, waiting for Gavin's footsteps on the stairs. Her eyes ached with unshed tears, and her whole being shook with utter humiliation. What he had thought of her before was as nothing to what he must think now. Restlessly she turned from side to side, trying in vain to find relief in sleep. But although she was exhausted beyond words, it eluded her, and she lay wide awake in the darkness, listening to the clock in the hall chiming each quarter of an hour away until it grew light. And then, at last, she slept.

She was awoken by a light tap on the door, and a voice saying:

'May I come in?'

For a few moments she lay there, fighting through various layers of sleep and realization, until, fully awake, and aware of where she was – and why – and what had happened – she sat up in bed.

The door handle was being rattled gently. 'Jane, are you awake?' It was Gavin. 'No,' she whispered. 'Oh, no – go away!' But it was too quiet for anyone to hear, and as the door finally opened, she lay quickly back on her pillow and pulled the sheets up. She didn't want him to see her, nor did she want to look at him, and she wondered if she would ever be able to look at him again.

'I've brought you coffee,' she heard him say, and it was hard to tell what there was in his tone.

She stayed where she was, rigid, sheets held tightly round her face, which she kept averted. 'Thank you.' Her voice was muffled, but he heard.

'It's eleven o'clock. Do you want anything to eat?'

'No, thank you. Just go away and leave me alone.'

She heard the cup go down, and then a second later, the door shut. Jane sat up. She drank the hot refreshing coffee, and went into the bathroom, determined not to stay a minute longer than necessary in Gavin's house.

She hated pulling the dress on again, but had no choice. She zipped it up as far as she could, combed her hair, and put on some lipstick. Her eyes were shadowed, her face pale with fatigue, but she didn't care. In a few minutes she would be away from here for good. And she would never enter his home again.

Jane picked up her bag and went to the door. With head held high, she walked downstairs.

She managed to put on a semblance of normality when she reached home and went in to her father. He greeted her fondly, looking with worried curiosity at her tired face.

'Gavin pushed a note through the door last night,' he said. 'What a shame that you couldn't get in. Still, I'm sure you were comfortable at Gavin's. He's an excellent host.'

'Oh yes,' Jane agreed. 'I didn't sleep very well, though. It was so late – and I can never sleep well in a strange bed.' She thought longingly of her own safe one upstairs. 'I think I'll have a bath and a lie down for a while. You don't mind?'

'Mind? This is your house, Jane, to do as you like. Have a rest for as long as you like. Mac will be over to lunch later. You met him, of course, last night?'

'Yes. I think he's a very nice man.' But she didn't want to think about that disastrous party, and it would be unavoidable when Mac arrived. Her father would certainly want to hear all about it then. She knew that she would feel better for a sleep. Perhaps, too, she needed time to think, privately . . .

Two hours later, rested and refreshed, and feeling more her normal self, Jane went downstairs, wearing one of the crisp cotton dresses that Megan had helped choose. It was a simple style, with a v-neck, straight bodice, and flared skirt, fashionably short – and cool. A dark rich green, it brought out the exciting shade of her eyes, and with her hair brushed back, but loose, Jane looked very young and fresh.

Mac was sitting with her father on the shady patio at the back of the house, and he rose to greet her with the words:

'I've been telling your dad how you were the belle of the ball.'

Jane laughed and shook her head. 'Don't believe him, Father. There were some beautiful women there.'

'Aye, but none like you,' Mac winked at her. '*La belle* Sara was in a pretty pet about you leaving with Gavin.'

Jane put a hand to her mouth. 'Oh! I ought to phone her to apologize for leaving before the end – and to thank her,' she added.

'Aye, well, she'll not be up awhile, I shouldn't wonder. Was it the rich food made you poorly?'

'Yes, and the champagne,' she admitted ruefully. 'I didn't realize how strong it really was.'

'Ach well, you have to learn some time, I suppose,' he grinned. 'And it was a good party. Broke up about three. I've not been up long myself.' He looked at her. 'Colin has your key, and a brown scarf. No doubt he'll be bringing them along later.'

'Oh, yes.' Jane felt a twinge of dismay, as if he would

only have to look at her to see what had happened – ridiculous, of course, but the thought lingered even after Ellen came in to say that lunch was ready.

They all ate on the patio, and Jane listened to Mac and her father talking together companionably, as old friends do. It gave her time to think, and inevitably, after a while, her thoughts went back irresistibly to Gavin. He had been out when she had gone downstairs just a few hours previously. The back door had been open, and there was no sign of Carlo either. Jane, in a fit of cowardice, had ripped a sheet from the shopping list that hung by the back door, and written: 'I have gone home. Thank you for your kind hospitality, Jane.' She had left the note on the table by her empty coffee cup, and, feeling like a thief in the night, had stolen quietly away.

Would Gavin come round? Yes, she thought, he would. Perhaps he had already forgotten the little incident, except as something to give him amusement when he thought of it. *That* was the sort of man he was. He thought of her as a child, a selfish, gold-digging one, but still a child. How much differently he behaved towards Sara! Jane still saw the look on his face when he had greeted her before the party, a mixture of such affection and intimacy that even now, at the thought of it, she had a twinge of some emotion she couldn't define. She would not discover for a long time just what that feeling was. She saw again Sara's face uplifted for Gavin's kiss, those beautiful features confident and assured. How wonderful it must be to be like that, thought Jane. To be full of your own inner assurance – to *know* that you were loved.

She put her spoon down. The delicious fluffy peach mousse tasted suddenly dry and cardboardy.

Mac glanced at her from under his thick brows. 'Hm, not dieting, I hope?'

Jane managed to laugh. 'No. I'm full, that's all.'

'Ah, too much to eat last night, I shouldn't wonder. One thing I'll say about Leonie, she does you proud with the food.'

'Yes, it was marvellous,' Jane agreed, and added silently, 'And I brought it all up on the way home.' She pushed back her chair. 'Will you excuse me?'

She went up to her room, pausing as always on her way to look at her father's pictures. She never ceased to be amazed at the depths of his talent, and each picture was now becoming as familiar to her as if she had lived with it for years. She gently touched her favourite, feeling the thick whorls of oil paint with her fingertips, on the scene of a child and dog staring forlornly out at a small boat on a calm blue sea.

With a little sigh she went on upstairs, and as she reached the top, heard the heavy knocker lifted and rapped firmly twice. Jane moved quietly on to the landing, waiting for Ellen to open the door, and stood out of sight as she heard the housekeeper's slippers flip-flopping from the kitchen. Her heart thudded, her mouth went dry, and she knew who it was even before she heard his voice.

'Hello, Ellen. Is John home?'

'Hello, Mr. Gavin. You should have woke me when you came home with Miss Jane—' Jane's fingers tightened involuntarily, on the banister top, '—I sure wouldn't have minded.'

She heard Gavin's laugh low, and amused, and found her heart pounding so hard that it almost hurt. 'I knew you needed your beauty sleep Ellen – and anyway, I was in no state to throw pebbles at windows. You'd have had something to say to me if I'd broken yours, wouldn't you—' their voices faded away down the hall, and Jane let out her breath slowly.

So he was here, and unless she was going to hide in her room for hours, she would have to go down and face him. It had to be done some time, and perhaps it would be less of a strain with Mac there as well. She went to the bedroom and sat at her dressing-table. She brushed her long silky hair back and applied fresh lipstick, a deep pink shade that she knew suited her. There was nothing that she could do about the slight smudges underneath her eyes – she didn't realize that they merely served to enhance her appearance of slender beauty, making her appear most delicate and appealing in a wholly feminine way.

Standing, Jane looked longingly at her bed, pulled a little face, took a deep breath, and went out of the room and downstairs. She paused in the living-room for a few moments to try and regain something of the determination she had felt upstairs. The men were faintly visible outside, partly hidden by a shady wall, but she could hear their voices, hear Gavin's laugh – and she nearly turned tail. Then, outwardly calm and serene but inwardly trembling, she went out, and said, as if surprised: 'Oh, hello, Gavin. Thank you again for your hospitality.'

He stood up, a tall powerful man whose very being was vibrant with strength and a kind of animal magnetism.

'Hello, Jane.' His eyes met hers, and whatever was in them was veiled. 'I nearly brought Carlo over with me. He was looking all over the house for you earlier.'

The words didn't really register. They were polite utterings, addressed as much to the other two men as to her. She saw a brief flicker of something on his face, almost a look of puzzlement – as if he had expected her to be different. . . . It added to Jane's perilously fragile confidence. She went over to her chair and sat down. She had managed the first and most difficult hurdle. She could take everything else in her stride – perhaps.

Conversation started, back and forth, mainly between the men, but they included Jane. Ellen came to clear away, and Jane sat there quietly, praying for Gavin to go. He kept glancing at her, but with each minute that passed she grew slightly more sure of herself, and she was able to return his looks calmly, even, sometimes, to smile.

There was a lull in the talk at one point, and she heard Gavin say: 'How's that project of yours coming along, Mac?'

Jane was watching Mac's face as Gavin spoke, and for a moment was puzzled by what she saw. Then Mac answered, one eyebrow lifted in apparent amusement, 'You mean the nursery school? Fine, but why—'

Gavin cut swiftly in, 'I wondered if you'd found anyone to replace Shirley yet?'

'Oh, Shirley!' Mac nodded slowly, and Jane watched. He had been about to say something – so why had Gavin interrupted as he had?

'No, I haven't, as a matter of fact. Volunteers aren't too easy to come by.' He grinned suddenly at the watching Jane. 'Now, I'd ask Jane, if she wasn't on holiday.'

Jane's curiosity was thoroughly aroused by now. She answered his grin with a smile, and asked: 'What would you ask me?'

He shrugged. 'Och, I'm only joking, Jane. I wouldn't dream—' but he looked quickly at Gavin as he spoke.

'Please,' she begged.

'Och, well,' he leaned forward towards her. 'We – er – I started a small pre-school group recently outside Port Patrick for the children of workers in the canning factory. It means we can recruit extra labour – which we need badly – from among the mothers of young children, say between three and six. It's still in the experimental stage, you understand.' His eyes lit up as he launched into something that was clearly dear to his heart. 'Megan comes down two days a week, and some others. Shirley Murray has been helping us too, but she's getting married next week, so we'll be stuck. We've been canvassing round, but without much success. I can't ask Megan to take on any more – though I've a feeling she would if I asked—' he shrugged apologetically. 'Now I'm on my hobbyhorse – you'll be sorry you asked.'

'But I'm not.' Jane was so interested that Gavin might not have been there. 'What exactly does the work entail?'

'The usual stuff. Some very elementary tuition, and keeping an eye on the children at play. They've got lettered bricks, books, toys and so on. But the thing is the good it does them. Already they look forward to coming, instead of playing in the open streets as they have been doing. We're getting more new pupils every week,' he added ruefully: 'It seems to have snowballed.'

'It sounds marvellous!' Jane breathed. She leaned forward, clasping her hands, unaware of Gavin's eyes on her, unaware too of the picture she made, her soft hair falling forward, shadowing her face, and she looked at her father, who missed nothing, and who was watching quietly. 'I'd like to help – that is – I—' she floundered, seeing his expression, and he said gently:

'I have no intention of stopping you – if you want to go.' He looked at Mac. 'Why not let Jane come one day, and look round? I have a feeling she would find it interesting.'

'But it means leaving you,' belatedly, she protested.

John laughed. 'It would only be for a few hours a day, Jane. There's not a lot of excitement for you here. I'd be glad for you to go – but only if it suits you.'

There was a small waiting silence, and during it Jane realized that Gavin hadn't uttered a word in this exchange. Somehow, it decided her.

'I'd like to help, Mac,' she said quietly. 'I passed for teacher training college just before I came out here. It will be good practice for me.'

'You will?' Mac threw back his head and laughed. 'You're a bonny lass, Jane. When? Tomorrow?'

She smiled. 'Yes, if you like. Father, is tomorrow all right with you?'

He nodded, and she was surprised to see some emotion on his face. 'Of course, Jane,' he reached out and patted her hand. 'I'm pleased with you.'

His words filled her with a warm glow, that was banished a moment later when Mac said: 'How will you get there?'

'I hadn't thought of that,' she admitted, dismayed.

Gavin spoke. 'I can take you at eight when I go into town, if that's any good.'

She looked at Mac in blind panic, hoping he would suggest an alternative, but he nodded in a pleased manner. 'If you could, Gavin. I'll fetch you back of course at four, Jane.'

She swallowed. There was no backing out now. If only she could drive! 'Thank you,' she said, and if it came out slightly ungraciously, she couldn't help it. 'I'm going to learn to drive,' she added quickly, 'so I'll be able to take myself then.'

Gavin's mouth quirked. 'It's not quite that easy, Jane,' he remarked.

She looked at him, seeing the patronizing smile, the air of supreme confidence he wore like a cloak, and said: 'I don't know till I try, do I?' Her eyes sparkled defiance.

'True,' he shrugged. 'My car's next door. Do you want a lesson now?'

She heard her father's and Mac's amused chuckles, and saw the slight smile that touched Gavin's mouth. He expected her to refuse! Eyes wide, she looked at him. 'Aren't you frightened I'd drive into the nearest tree?'

'Not if you're not,' was the calm reply.

'Then you're on!' She didn't know why she said it – it was as though the words had come out on their own – and then she went cold as he stood up.

'Excuse me, I'll only be a few minutes.' He went into the house without a backward glance, a tall, arrogant, powerful creature who walked with an easy, tiger-like grace. Jane looked at her father. What had she done? There was a momentary pause after he had gone, then she heard Mac's quiet laugh. 'Och, you do me a power of good, Jane.'

She looked at him, then reluctantly smiled. 'He gets my back up,' she confessed.

'I can see that!' Mac looked at John, who was watching Jane with warm affection in his glance, and said to him: 'You've a spirited lass here, you know, John?'

Her father nodded slowly. 'I'm beginning to think so,' he agreed solemnly.

'I'm sorry, Father.' Jane felt as if she ought to apologize. 'I don't like being rude to your guest, but—'

'Jane, don't say anything,' he lifted a hand. 'Gavin enjoys these little exchanges, wouldn't you say, Mac?'

'Aye. He's so used to everyone agreeing with him, I don't doubt it's a refreshing change to meet someone who's not afraid to speak her mind.'

If only you knew! she thought, swallowing something that was between a sob and a laugh. If only you knew!

Footsteps prevented her answering him, fortunately,

and she looked up to see Gavin coming out. She ran her tongue over her lips. What on earth had she done now?

Gavin looked down at her from his six feet plus. 'Ready?' he inquired.

'Yes,' she stood up. 'I won't be long, Father. Will you be here when I get back?' this to Mac, who nodded, smiling.

'That I will. Off you go.'

She went back through the living-room, regretting her foolish acceptance of that man's challenge. What madness had possessed her? After all that had happened – to think she had vowed never—

'Nervous?' he asked softly as he opened the front door and gestured for her to go first.

'No. Should I be?' she answered. But she was – terribly so, and in a way she didn't understand. She hesitated on the steps, and nearly stumbled – and perhaps he understood that hesitation, for he said: 'Nobody's forcing you, you know,' but he smiled softly when he said it.

Fire sparked inside her. She turned swiftly on him. 'Wouldn't you love it if I backed out?' she gritted, marching over to the driver's door of that low-slung, sleek, *powerful* Mercedes.

'Wait a moment,' he was going to ignore her remark. 'You get in the passenger seat for a while. Watch me drive first – then it's your turn.'

She paused, then, with a shrug, walked slowly to the passenger door. He had it open before she reached it, closed it after her, then went round to the driver's seat. Sudden panic filled Jane. It was all very well for her to put on a brave face – but what if she really did make a mess of everything? She knew that this would not be a patient man. She determind to watch everything he did very carefully – and remembered it.

He switched on the engine, released the handbrake, changed into first gear, his eyes questioningly on her as he did so. She nodded slightly: 'I'm watching.'

'This is the clutch,' his foot tapped on the middle pedal. 'An easy way to remember the three pedals is by saying your ABC backwards.' He pointed. 'Clutch – brake – accelerator.' He grinned. 'Got that?'

'Yes.'

'Good.' The car sprang forward, and they went down the drive. Instead of turning left in the direction of Port Patrick, he turned right, and Jane asked: 'Where are we going?'

'To the airport. There's nothing doing there on a Sunday. You'll have all the space you need to drive.'

Jane couldn't resist it. 'No trees, you mean?' she said sweetly.

He began to laugh. It was almost as if he were genuinely amused, and she felt her fists clench involuntarily.

'If you like.' He turned a cynically amused glance on her. 'You're never lost for an answer, are you?'

'With you – no,' she answered shortly. Why, oh, why couldn't she learn to keep her mouth shut? She was never like this with anyone else, but there was something about him that roused an almost primitive instinct to retaliate within her. She could never win, she knew that even before he answered, his eyes travelling briefly to her tightened hands on her lap.

'And are you always so tense, or is that just with me as well?' he asked coolly.

'I'm not tense,' she answered, fighting for calm. 'I – I'm trying to concentrate on what you're doing. You told me to watch.'

'My apologies.' Laughter lurked in his voice, that arrogant amusement she found so maddening about him.

Why did everyone like him? That was something she felt sure she would never understand. He was imperious, completely overbearing – and one of those people, like Aunt Dorothy, who were always right – who *had* to be right, or they were unbearable to live with, or be with.

'Now, watch this.' His voice interrupted her thoughts, and she obeyed. He was giving her a lesson – she really must concentrate and forget all personal animosity, which could only harm her. He was changing to a lower gear and slowing down as they neared a crossroads. There was not a soul to be seen anywhere, and in fact they hadn't seen anyone since setting off. It was as if the island slept.

'I know there are no other cars, but it's always essential to slow down at crossroads – it will help you to remember when you're driving into Port Patrick,' he remarked, as if he had read her thoughts.

'Yes, I see,' Jane answered. If only he would stick to this impersonal tone, he would be almost bearable – almost.

'Only a couple of miles further, and you can take over. Okay?' He was looking ahead, not at her, and Jane was able to study his profile unobserved. His chin was a determined one, a strong chin, matching that strength in his profile, lean and powerful. He wore a plain white cotton shirt, short-sleeved and open-necked. His arms were tanned and muscular, covered with thick black hair, the darkness accentuated by the flat broad silver watch-strap on his left wrist. And those arms had . . . Jane took a deep breath and looked out of the window. Stop it, she told herself fiercely – stop it!

'Yes,' she answered belatedly. 'Thanks.'

'Don't thank me,' he answered. 'I've never taught anyone to drive before – I might learn something myself.'

Jane didn't answer. What could he learn from her – except that he was even more perfect than he had supposed? She bit her lip to stop a laugh escaping.

Suddenly he was slowing down. They were on the perimeter of the huge primitive airfield, which was strangely quiet and deserted. Gavin switched off the engine. 'All right. Move over, we'll change places,' he said crisply, and got out. Jane slid over and gripped the wheel, still warm from his hands. This is ridiculous, she thought wildly. Here am I, about to learn driving from the man I've vowed to avoid completely, and he'll be watching every move I make – and I've got to stick it out for an hour or more!

Then he was beside her, and sitting with one long arm along the back of the seat. 'Okay? Switch on. Foot on clutch – clutch,' he repeated, as she put her left foot on the brake in the middle. She moved it quickly. 'Now, first gear – and off we go. Right foot gently on accelerator – *gently*.'

The car moved forward jerkily at first, then, as Jane got the feel of the accelerator, more smoothly.

'Right, I'll change to second, keep your foot on the clutch—' His voice was calm, and as she obeyed his instructions, Jane felt her tense body begin to relax, found too that the sensation of being in control – almost – of the beautiful vehicle was a stimulating experience. Once his hand came over briefly and moved hers on the steering wheel. A swift light touch that lasted only seconds as he said: 'Remember to keep your hands in the ten-to-two position. Right?'

'Right.' She nodded without taking her eyes from the tarmac ahead, rapidly being swallowed beneath them as they sped along.

'Forget about the gears for a while. I want you to get the feel of the car. I'll do the changing for you. Just remember to press the clutch when I say. Understand?'

'Yes.' She was obeying him instantly, she found, with no confusion or hesitation. She realized suddenly, too, that she was actually enjoying herself – much to her surprise. They drove round the outer boundaries of the field, passed three hangars, shimmering in the heat, and came back to their starting point, where he told her to stop.

'You've done well,' he said it almost approvingly, and Jane felt a sudden lurch of her heart, followed by a warm glow. How absurd! As if she *cared* – but oddly, she did.

'We'll do that again, but first let me show you the gears ...'

An hour later they stopped by the main hut of the airport – the one that had first bade her welcome to Saramanca, and on Gavin's instructions Jane switched off the engine and applied the handbrake. She was perspiring freely, and her whole body ached with the concentration of the last hour. Almost numbly she sat there waiting for him to speak.

'All right, Jane, we'll have a rest now. Come on, get out and stretch your legs – you need a break.'

She got out, surprised at just how stiff and trembly her limbs were, and found him watching her with amusement. 'Need any help walking?' he inquired dryly.

'No, thanks.' She straightened her aching back and flexed and unflexed her fingers. 'Where are we going?' She looked round her.

'You'll see. This way.'

She followed him round the back of the Nissen hut, and he produced a key from his trouser pocket and unlocked the door. They went inside the large bare, airless building, strangely deserted and forlorn with the rows of empty counters, luggage trolleys lined up neatly against the wall. Their footsteps echoed hollowly on the concrete floor as he led the way to a door at the end, and she found that she was whispering in some alarm: 'But there's no one – are we allowed—?'

'Yes!' He echoed her whispering tone and slowed down to take her arm in a curiously protective gesture. 'There's a kitchen at the end, with a fridge full of ice and drinks. You do want one, don't you?'

His fingers burned like fire on her bare arm, and she was almost relieved when he took his hand away as he opened the door and stood back for her to go in. The small room was even hotter than the main one, and perspiration broke out afresh on Jane's forehead. Gavin indicated a chair, and she flopped limply into it.

He put two glasses on the table and opened an enormous white refrigerator that throbbed noisily in a corner. Taking out two cans of beer, he flung ice cubes into the glasses and opened the cans, which spurted and hissed. Looking at her, he said: 'There is only beer, I'm afraid. Will it do?'

She nodded weakly. 'Anything at all.'

'It really isn't strong, I promise you.' The foaming golden liquid cascaded over the ice, and Jane watched it with cardboard-dry mouth and parched lips. It was the most delicious drink she had ever had in her life. She ignored his admonition to take it slowly, and finished the glassful in seconds. He filled it again, emptying the can and then flinging it into a bin before casually pulling up a chair for himself. He sat straddling the seat, his arms along the back. And he watched Jane, his glance cool and level as he said: 'You've driven well. Have you had enough for today?'

'I'll leave that to you,' she answered, running a finger

down the icy glass. She found that she couldn't meet his glance, which was disconcerting. Perhaps it was the effect of the beer, but her legs were feeling decidedly woolly.

'I think you've had enough. You look tired. But it's up to you.'

'I don't want to take up any more of your time,' she answered uneasily.

He shrugged, lifted his glass and took a long swallow. 'Okay, that's it for today. I'll give you another lesson as soon as I can, and you'll be driving yourself in no time.' That jerked her head up disbelievingly to meet his glance, and he smiled, his teeth very white.

'I'm not joking. You're a natural.' He paused, then added: 'May I ask you something?'

Panic flared briefly. Was he going to mention—? His voice went on quickly, as if he realized her thoughts. 'About Mac.'

'Oh! What?' Her heart settled down again.

'Why did you offer to help at the – his school?'

The question was so unexpected that she frowned. 'Why?' she answered slowly. 'Because – because I wanted to. It sounds interesting.' And now their eyes met. 'Why do you ask?'

He rubbed his chin. 'You're on holiday. Nobody would expect you to volunteer—'

'No?' And the picture came back to her, of how it had been, there on the patio, at her father's house, of how Gavin had brought the subject up in the first place, the look on Mac's face when he had – and Gavin's quick interruption when the doctor had been about to say something. Jane felt as if she were on the verge of some discovery – but she knew not what – only that Gavin, for some reason of his own had known what Mac would ask. She took a deep breath and met his eyes again questioningly. And softly, knowing she must take care now, she asked him: 'Tell me something. You brought the subject up in the first place. You *knew* that Mac would hope I – I–' seeing his eyes, she floundered. But she had to go on now that she had begun. She *needed* to know. 'You did it for a purpose. What was it?' And now she held his deep, cool, unfathomable gaze with her own.

He smiled and held up his right hand. 'You're very shrewd, Jane.'

She gripped her glass tightly. 'I've just asked you a question,' she said doggedly.

'Then you shall have an answer.' His voice was decidedly soft. 'I had a reason. I wanted to know whether you would volunteer – or not.'

'Why?' she persisted.

'Because – oh, put it down to curiosity.' And he stared at her as if challenging her to ask any more.

'You thought I wouldn't, didn't you?'

'All right, yes, I did.'

She let out her breath, stood up and swept her bag from the table. Frightening anger filled her in a sudden hot wave. She felt as if she would choke if she didn't get out. 'I'm sorry I disappointed you,' she spat out. 'Now, I'd like to go home – please.'

He stood up slowly and then took the glasses to the sink, turned on the tap and rinsed them. She waited, seething, by the door. Then he looked at her, seeing the spots of colour burning in her cheeks, and said:

'I've made you angry.'

She had to fight for control before answering. 'Yes, you have. Who the *hell* do you think you are?'

'I told you the truth. I don't tell lies. Would you have liked me to say no?'

'What right have *you* to go around—' she struggled for

the right words, '—*testing* people like that? You're insufferably arrogant – and I suppose you thought I'd make a complete fool of myself in the car as well, didn't you?'

'No, as a matter of fact I didn't. And you won't get anywhere by losing your temper with me.'

'Oh no!' She gave a disbelieving laugh. 'You – you – think you own everybody – can do just as *you* like. Well, you can't with me, *Mister* Grant. I'm not some poor old Chinese woman to be pushed around, I can t-tell you!' She was almost trembling with the uncontrollable urge to hit him – or cry – or both.

He walked over to her and stopped. 'Chinese woman? You've lost me completely.'

'I suppose you've forgotten! That doesn't surprise me!' She turned to open the door and get out of that suffocating room, and away from him, but he put out his arm and pressed it shut again.

'Not yet—'

She whirled round. 'Open this door!' she demanded. I'm not stopping here a minute longer with *you*!'

'Oh yes, you are.' And he smiled. 'Until you tell me the meaning of that rather sinister crack.'

'I saw you at Gaver airport – I'm quite sure you didn't see *me*. You were far too busy laying the law down to a crowd of officials, stopping this poor old woman from getting on the plane. Where did they take her to? The torture chambers?'

And then he did the unforgivable. He began to laugh. Softly at first, then throwing back his head helplessly. 'Oh, my God!' he managed to say at last. 'So that's what it looked like!' He sobered up and looked at Jane's furious face. 'You're really serious, aren't you?'

For answer Jane turned the door handle. He swung her

round, his fingers biting into her arms like steel.

'Tell me,' he said – softly, dangerously.

'I don't want to *speak* to you. And take your hands off me at once!'

Slowly he did so. 'Right,' he said. 'I'm taking you to the school tomorrow. Remind me, when we get there, to show you something. On second thoughts, you won't need to. I'll show you anyway.' His eyes glinted, darker and more penetrating than ever. 'And *then* I hope you'll retract your words. Let's go.'

CHAPTER SEVEN

JANE was too tired to think when she went to bed that night. So many things had happened since the driving lesson, and the awful quarrel with Gavin. He had left her at her front door and gone home, after they had driven there in electric, pulsating silence. Colin had arrived in the evening with her scarf and key, and they had walked down to the beach, where he had tried to put his arms round her. But Jane had stopped him. She didn't want him to kiss her, but she didn't know why, except perhaps that the memory of a certain other embrace was still too painful and vivid . . .

Mac had remained throughout Colin's visit, and when he was about to leave, had asked Jane to see him to his car, leaving John in the living room pleasantly tired after several games of chess, and obviously much better than he had been on the previous day.

'Megan's told you I want your father to go for examination and tests by a specialist, hasn't she?' he began, without preamble.

'Yes. But haven't you any idea what's wrong with him?' she asked, as they reached the car.

Mac shook his head. 'It's nothing I've encountered before. He gets tired easily, and then he gets these attacks where his arms are useless – like some form of temporary paralysis. I've tried various drugs, but I'm not an expert on this kind of thing, and frankly I'd feel happier if he did see someone – but he won't. Says it's nothing, and he has faith in me – but if you could talk to him you might do the trick, Jane.'

'I'll do my best, I promise you, Mac, but I mustn't rush it or he'll guess—'

He patted her shoulder in a fatherly manner, those startling blue eyes glinting with good humour. 'I ken fine you will, lass. How long are you here for?'

'A month – but I think I might—'. she hesitated, '—might stay longer. I w-want to, and he's asked me, so—' She stopped and looked at him, and he grinned.

'I hope you do, Jane. I really hope you do. He's different already – I saw that today. He's a lonely man. Och, he's got lots of friends – and a lot more would like to be, I don't doubt – but he's choosey, thank the lord. Until you came, he was living in a vacuum. Even his painting had palled – and that's a tragedy, with his talent. Now – well, it wouldn't surprise me to see him start again. He's found his daughter – someone to live for. The sooner you can drive the better. Take him out and about, then we'll really see a difference. How did the lesson go on with Gavin, by the way? I didn't like to ask when you came back. You seemed a little—' he rubbed his bald head thoughtfully, '— a little distrait. Did it not go well?'

Jane had to smile at his diffident manner. 'Yes and no,' she admitted. 'He says I'm doing well, but—' and she stopped.

'But he's an arrogant, bossy devil?'

'I didn't say that—' she began, horrified.

He chuckled richly. 'Aye, well, you don't need to, lass. I can see it. I know him better than anyone – knew his father too, for years. I get along with him fine. I like and respect him too. He's dead straight and honest, is Gavin. And a grand man to have on your side in a fight – though *that's* quite another story – but I can see his faults too. He's been so used to having everyone fall over themselves to agree with him, ever since he was a young pup, that he's come to expect it. He can no more help it than you can breathing – and it's maybe not his fault. That's the effect that money has – not on the possessor, but on most of the people he meets. They're scared stiff to offend him. Just be yourself, Jane, don't let him bully you.'

'I won't.' She shook her head slowly. 'But it's difficult—' she liked and trusted this outspoken Scot, and she knew she could talk to him in a way she would have hesitated to with most others. She went on: 'I lived with an aunt for several years, since my mother died. She's the same as Gavin in an odd way. I was right under her thumb – but since coming out here to Saramanca, I've realized just how wrong she was in so many ways. I suppose, in a sense, I resent him because of her. Do you know what I mean?'

'I'm no psychiatrist, but yes, I do. Och, Jane,' he patted her arm, 'you do me good – you're doing your dad a power of good – and I think you'll do Gavin good as well.' And with those rather puzzling words, he got into his car, and drove off, still laughing. Jane was too tired to even try and analyse his meaning.

She was ready sharp at eight the following morning. Mac had told her to wear something easily washed – she was soon to discover why! – so she donned a pair of the shorts she had bought with Megan the previous week. They were brief, bright blue, and had the effect of making her legs look very long, slender and tanned. She pulled on a plain white tee-shirt, slipped on her sandals, and went down to await Gavin's arrival. Ellen was fascinated to hear where she was going.

'You'll have your hands full, child,' she remarked, as she gave Jane a hearty breakfast of fluffy omelette with cheese, a beaker of ice-cold milk, and sweet, honey-drenched pancakes to round it all off. 'So eat up – you'll need your strength!'

Jane obeyed, and began to wonder exactly what she was letting herself in for!

She had barely finished when the knock came at the door, and she stood up hastily, grabbing for her beaker of milk, still unfinished. 'Don't you fret now. Mister Gavin can wait a moment,' the housekeeper bustled away tut-tutting, and Jane thought – that's one person who's not scared of him, anyway. She finished the milk and went into the hall, calling up to tell her father that she was going. His voice came faintly down: 'Don't work too hard!'

'I won't,' she assured him. 'Goodbye.'

Gavin stood by the car with Ellen. She seemed to be telling him something, and stopped as she heard Jane. They both turned, and Jane saw his eyes travel slowly down her in silent assessment before he nodded coolly, and said: 'Good morning, Jane.'

'Good morning.' And then she remembered his words of the previous day. Where was he taking her? Why, oh, why hadn't she kept her mouth shut? Why in fact was she *always* opening it so wide – with him?

They drove out of the drive, watched by Ellen, who waved, then turned to go in. Tremulously Jane asked: 'Where are we going?'

'You'll see,' was the brief answer. He was different – almost like he had been when they had first met; subtly and frighteningly hostile. Jane felt her hackles rise. The sooner they were done, the better. And how Sara could want to marry him was beyond her comprehension. He was moody, unpredictable, and arrogant. No amount of money in the world could compensate for that. He broke into her thoughts: 'You might be disappointed with the school. There are only women and children there.' And his glance slid down her legs as he spoke, and Jane felt her body grow warm at the note, almost a sneer, in his voice.

Biting back an angry retort, she managed to say calmly: 'I don't think I understand you.'

'I think you do,' he shot back. 'There'll be no men to impress, so the sexy outfit will be wasted.'

She gritted her teeth. 'Are you trying to be deliberately rude? Because if so, you're succeeding. And f-for your information, I'm dressed like this because Mac told me to wear something easily cleaned. I wasn't aware I was dressed improperly.'

He gave a short laugh. 'I wouldn't say it's improper – far from it.' But he made it sound insulting.

'No? Tell me, what do *you* wear when you're swimming? *If* you go swimming, that is.'

'Trunks. And that has nothing whatever to do with it.'

'Perhaps not. Anyway,' she finished, 'as I'm sure you're aware, I'm scarcely more than a child, so it can hardly matter what I wear!' It was a silly thing to say, she knew, but that was how he made her feel – but she wasn't prepared for his reaction, for the sudden cold hardening of his face, the way his hands tightened on the wheel so that his knuckles showed white. She took a deep apprehensive breath. What had she said *now*?

The anger – but was it anger? – in his voice made it harsh as he ground out: 'I don't need reminding of your age.'

Then there was silence. A puzzled, disturbing silence that went on as he accelerated along the broad white surface that was being swallowed up under the wheels of the Mercedes. Jane turned away and looked out of the window, knowing that there was nothing more to say. For some reason her casual, thoughtless answer had silenced him effectively. She though she would never know why — but she was wrong.

He drove through Port Patrick, the streets already abustle with life and colour, and there was such a tension in that car that she wished she were out among those people. How much further? she wondered, but dared not ask. She must wait and see.

The character of the island changed subtly once the town had been left behind them. It was more exotic, with the mountain range even nearer, and flowers and lush tropical plants growing in even greater profusion, encroaching almost on to the road. The sheer wild beauty took Jane's breath away. At times the tall trees nearly met across the road so that they seemed to be driving through a high green tunnel, with the sun occasionally piercing the thick leaves in brilliant yellow diamond flashes. Gavin slowed, then turned right down a slightly narrower track, and she saw in the distance through the trees, several long low sheds with corrugated iron roofs that were painted dazzling white to reflect the heat. Mac's car was parked by a tree, and Gavin drew up behind it and switched off.

'Right. We're here,' he said.

Jane opened her door and stepped out, feeling the intense heat strike immediately. She watched Gavin, wondering why he wore such casual clothes to work; tan shirt and matching linen slacks with his bare feet thrust into thonged sandals, and his hair brushed casually back. Her lip curled. He was law unto himself — how could she forget it? And what could he possibly be going to show her *here* at the school? As if in answer to her thoughts, he said: 'First, I want to show you something.'

And he marched away, leaving her to follow. Through heavy bushes, overgrown with waxy white flowers, heavily scented, almost overpowering, he went, and Jane, her mouth tightening rebelliously, followed. Then suddenly they were in a clearing, and water tinkled in the distance, lending an air of charm to the several small houses in a rough semi-circle. Bushes of bright flowers lined the walls, small lawns had been painstakingly watered to keep them a rich green, and every house was brightly painted, with shutters open to admit all possible air.

Gavin stopped, and turned. 'Ready?' he inquired, and his face was giving nothing away.

There was the tiniest tremor in Jane's voice as she answered: 'For what?'

He lifted a sarcastic eyebrow. 'Why, to see the results of the old Chinese woman's visit to the torture chamber.' And without looking back, he went to the nearest door and knocked on it.

Now at last she was going to find out the truth. Jane's heart hammered against her ribs as the door opened. There was a split second of silence, then Gavin was surrounded by people – all Chinese, several children, two or three young people, and a strangely familiar figure, who stood in the doorway surrounded also by a babel of voices as they all greeted Gavin. The old woman lifted her hand in a gesture of welcome, a broad smile splitting her parchment face nearly in two.

She came forward slowly, bowed, and took his hand, and Gavin turned, as if to say: 'See?'

Jane was drawn irresistibly forward. She didn't understand anything, but his look was challenging. Then he began to speak softly to the woman, and she nodded and turned bright button eyes on Jane, her smile broadening to reveal glints of gold in her teeth.

'Yes – yes – hello—' haltingly she spoke, and reached out a hand for Jane to take.

'She doesn't speak English,' Gavin said. 'But her grand-daughter wants to translate.' The youngest girl stepped forward, bowed and nodded as Gavin said something briefly to her. She turned to her grandmother, and there followed a rapid exchange of words which ended with the girl turning back to Jane and saying, in a pleasant sing-song voice: 'My grandmother wishes to thank you for your concern. If Mr. Grant had not been at the airport, she would not be here now.'

Jane swallowed, tried to smile, fully aware of Gavin's mocking glance resting on her. He wasn't going to help her. She took a deep breath. 'Oh! I wondered w-what was happening.'

'Yes, yes. Grandmother had come from Saigon all alone – had lost passport and money. The officials were going to call the police – they did not believe her, you see, think she is stowaway—' Jane nodded faintly at the girl's smile. 'Mr. Grant make them look after her, and guaran – guaranteed—' she stumbled over the word – 'that he would check up at this end and ring them back. Then he pay for them to give her a meal while she waits for him to telephone back from Saramanca. She was very hungry – she had been waiting at the airport for some hours.'

So that was where she had been taken – not to some unknown horror, but for a meal!

'Thank you for telling me. I'm so glad your grand-mother arrived safely,' she said. She was too stunned to say more. She waited as the voices broke out afresh, and the children, solemn little brown-eyed urchins, eyed her unblinkingly. Gavin seemed to be refusing an invitation, his hands going up apologetically, eloquently, as he backed away. There was a chorus of farewells, the young girl called Jane: 'You will come again, please?' And then he was taking her arm, and they were going back through the thick undergrowth.

Half way along, when they were completely out of sight of life, he stopped. 'Satisfied *now* that I'm not an ogre?'

Jane turned round. 'All right, you've had your fun. Yes, what would you like me to do – grovel? You could have just *told* me, couldn't you?' Her eyes sparkled.

'And would you have believed me?' he asked softly.

'I would have accepted it, yes.'

His mouth slanted crookedly. 'That's not quite the same thing. I wanted you to see for yourself. Just so that you would know the truth – and that things aren't necessarily what they seem to be.'

Jane, too disturbed to care what she did, said: 'Perhaps you should try and remember that too!'

His eyes narrowed. 'You've said something like that before. What do you mean?'

'Find out,' she shot back angrily. 'But I'm sure you've got a very good idea what I'm talking about.'

'Maybe. But I want you to tell me,' he said softly.

'Then you'll have to wait until I'm ready. I came to do some work. I'm sure Mac will be waiting.'

He made a small wordless exclamation, and stared down at her. Inside, her heart fluttered madly. He was so tall, and so strong – and yet suddenly she was no longer afraid of him. It was the oddest sensation, something new. As she looked at him, that big man who ruled everyone – who could make everyone do his bidding, she experienced almost a feeling of exultation. He couldn't hurt her any more by his words or actions. She looked up at him, her slender figure and face completely and utterly feminine, and faced him, this man, so aggressive, virility personified – and she knew that he sensed it too. Nothing could ever be put into words – but it was there – a secret that they shared, however unwillingly.

Jane turned and walked on, and she knew that something in that instant had changed. Nothing would ever be quite the same again.

The school was in another clearing, the children already there and waiting as Mac took her to them. It was a similar building to the others, long and low and wooden, with a corrugated iron roof. But the entire side opened out in a series of louvred doors, and from the outside she could see the shady interior with small chairs and camp beds and tables. In the clearing were slides and swings and a tiny roundabout, the sort Jane remembered from her childhood, one she had always known as a 'Spider's Web'. A pleasant-faced woman, in a plain blue smock, came over, followed by the more adventurous children, who were almost all uniformly dressed in little pants and nothing else. Their skins were honey-coloured, eyes nearly black, and they all looked plump and happy.

'I'm Ann Murray,' the woman said, before Mac had time to introduce them. 'And am I pleased to meet you!'

Jane looked round and laughed, shook hands with the woman, who was probably near to Megan's age, and said: 'I don't know much about nursery schools, I'm afraid.'

'But you will – you will.' Mrs Murray looked at Jane's outfit with approving eyes. 'I wish I could wear shorts,' she sighed. 'But my husband tells me I'm too old!'

Mac snorted. 'He's frightened you'll have all the men after you,' he answered. 'Well, I'll leave you ladies to it. I've a surgery in town, but I'll be back later.' And he waved and went off.

Mrs. Murray sighed. 'He's so busy,' she said. 'I don't know how he finds time for everything. Still, he thinks *we're* busy. Now,' she looked round them and gestured with her hand. 'You can see our equipment. All we have to do is keep an eye on them so that they don't fall off – or run off – and of course, we've got little books in the schoolroom. Come on,' she took Jane's arm. 'I'll show you. You can play now, children. Miss Ritchie has come to help me today, so let her see how nicely you behave.'

The children giggled, and some ran to the swings, but a few stayed silently watching. One solemn-faced little girl with a pigtail, her thumb firmly in her mouth, came up to Jane, removed the thumb, and held out her arms to be picked up. 'Please,' she said. 'Please carry.'

Jane bent and swung her up in her arms, surprised to feel how light she was. Mrs. Murray smiled. 'That's Melanie,' she said. 'She'll let you carry her about all day long – your arms will soon get tired if you're not firm with her.'

Melanie chuckled and put a chubby, slightly sticky hand on Jane's neck. And Jane knew then what Mac had meant about easily laundered clothing. 'I like you,' the little girl announced clearly. 'You're my friend.'

Jane, still carrying the child, followed Mrs. Murray into the warm airless room. It took her eyes a few seconds to adjust after the brilliance of the light outside, then she saw the books on the tables, with large clear pictures, bricks piled up on the floor, and teddies and dolls lying around to trip the unwary.

'Mac tells me you're going in for teaching,' Mrs. Murray remarked, as she bent to pick up an engine from the floor.

'Yes,' Jane smiled. 'This should be good practice for

me. How often do you come, Mrs. Murray?'

'Call me Ann, dear,' the other replied. 'Oh, twice a week if I can manage it. My daughter Shirley comes as well, but she's getting married Saturday and Mac's been going frantic.' She pulled a face. 'I must say, it seems a bit awful to expect you to do this on your holiday when you should be swimming and sunbathing – and especially as you haven't seen your father for so long.'

'I don't mind,' Jane assured her. 'There's plenty of time to do all the things I want to later – and my father seems to be glad that I said I'd come. And I like to help, really.'

Ann looked at her thoughtfully, then smiled. 'Yes, I'm sure you do. Just wait until four o'clock until you finally decide, though!'

Whether it was because she was new to it, or because the children were really well behaved, Jane didn't know, but she found it all tremendous fun.

At noon, two men brought large pans of food over from the works canteen, and the children sat down at the tables to eat. Ann and Jane ate theirs at the same time, a tasty concoction of rice, meat and fruit, with long drinks of fresh orange juice to follow.

Afterwards the children had a rest, and Ann, after settling the last one down looked along the row of camp beds each with a tiny figure on it and gave a huge sigh of relief. 'An hour to call our own,' she said. 'Come on, we'll have an iced coffee and a cigarette by that tree. We deserve it!'

The two women sat and chatted idly in the shade of a huge gnarled tree whose leaves rustled dryly in a faint breeze. Jane heard a car stop in the distance, and wondered idly if Mac had returned, then forgot about it as Ann said: 'You know, you must come to the wedding on

Saturday. I didn't know about your arrival when we sent the invitations out, or I'd have included you on your dad's.'

'That's very kind of you,' Jane began. 'Thank you. Is my father going?'

Ann shrugged. 'We don't know yet. Mac will tell us later on. We're having a running buffet, so it's not as if we have to know. We're leaving it entirely to him, Jane. But even if he doesn't, you must. Megan or Gavin will bring you, I'm sure.'

Gavin won't, thought Jane. Not if I can help it. But all she said was: 'Thank you – I'll mention it to Megan when I see her.'

The rest period soon passed, and the children began to stir as if at some unseen signal. Ann yawned and got to her feet, stretching. 'That's it. We'll give the older ones some instruction this afternoon, I think. They love learning.'

'Do their parents all work at the canning factory?' Jane asked curiously as they made their way back to the schoolroom.

'Yes, or in the copra sheds. We've got a flourishing export business in copra and coir – that's the heavy husks of coconuts, used to make mats and things. They're exported all over the world. Gradually, of course, as the business expands, the school will be put on a proper footing, with trained staff and more equipment It's still running as an experiment at the moment, so he just has a few of us coming in when we can – and glad to do it for him. He's done a lot for Saramanca, and everyone on it, one way or another.'

'Mac? Has he? He does seem very—' Jane began, to be stopped by Ann's surprised laughter.

'No, I don't mean Mac – *Gavin*. This is all Gavin's.

139

Everything.' She waved her arms wide.

Jane was quite unable to take it in for several moments. She stood there blankly staring at Ann. 'I – I don't think I understand,' she said slowly. 'I thought this school was Mac's.'

'Well, yes, in a way. They thought it out between them, Mac and Gavin.' She frowned. 'Do you mean to say nobody told you? Strange men!' She shook her head. 'Still, they're all a bit odd, I've always said.' She laughed at Jane's shocked face. 'It's Gavin's factory – as it was his father's before him. Mac advises him on health safe-guards and working conditions. Between the two of them, they've raised the standard of living on the island quite a bit. Now this,' she nodded at the swings, 'means that young mothers who were tied at home can work here and know their children are safe. A bus comes at quarter to four and takes them to Port Patrick in time for them to meet their older children from school.'

Jane was barely listening. Her mind went back irre-sistibly to that conversation on her father's patio. Now she knew why Mac had been interrupted by Gavin. And later, at the airfield – he could have told her then, but for strange reasons of his own, had not.

'I had no idea,' she felt she had to explain to the woman, whose face reflected her honest concern. 'I just took it, when Mac told me about it, that it was his idea.' They entered the large room and began rousing the few children who had not yet got up. Melanie swung her feet to the floor and went up to Jane, pushing her tiny hand into hers.

'I see you've made a friend,' Ann grinned. 'She might do as she's told for you, you never know.'

'She looks a good little girl to me,' Jane smiled down at the trusting face uplifted to her own, and Ann laughed.

'Mmm, I'll let you find out for yourself. She has a habit of trying to W-A-N-D-E-R O-F-F,' she spelt, with a warning look at the alert child.

Jane nodded. 'I get the message. I'll keep my eyes open.'

Later, as she played with the children in the playground, she remembered Ann's words, and looked round to reassure herself that all was well. Quickly she stood up. 'Melanie?' Jane turned to the school house. 'Is she there?'

Ann appeared. 'Oh, no, not again! When did you last see her?'

'Just a minute ago – she was in the sandpit—'

'She won't be far. Try that path.' Ann pointed. 'I'll go round the back. Stay playing for a moment, children.'

Jane ran quickly towards the track in the tangled undergrowth, assailed by sudden panic. Everything was so overgrown – the little girl could be anywhere ... She spun dizzily round as her foot caught in a wandering creeper, picked herself up, ignoring the pain that shot up from her ankle, and ran on crying out: 'Melanie, yoo-hoo, Melanie, where are you—' then she stopped. She was now near the other clearing, where Mac's car had been, leading off to the factory. But it wasn't Mac's car she saw, it was Gavin's. And beside it were two familiar figures. Jane registered the scene with sudden relief, and the picture they made, although she did not know it then, was to be etched in her memory for ever.

Gavin was bending to lift Melanie. For a moment Jane was unseen, and something made her halt in the shadows of the huge trees around her. She saw the tall man swing the small chubby half-naked child into his arms, heard her shriek of laughter, and his voice: 'Where are you going, Melanie?' And his tone was oddly gentle, causing

Jane's heart to lurch in a very strange manner. She stood there watching, heard the little girl's whispered reply, and then Gavin's: 'You can't go for walks without telling anyone! I'd better take you back, hadn't I?'

Then he saw Jane, and stopped. She stepped forward, wincing with pain as she put her left foot on the ground.

'Melanie!' she cried. Gavin walked towards her. His face tightened as he looked slowly down to her feet, then up to her face.

'Been running?' he asked softly.

'Yes. Thank you for stopping Melanie. I'll take her back now.'

'Perhaps I'd better do it. You don't look too fit to me.'

'I'm quite all right,' Jane answered. 'I tripped, that's all.'

'So I see. Does your foot hurt?'

'No,' she lied, and turning, began to walk back. Every step was torture, but she gritted her teeth, determined not to let him see. How could she have thought, even for a moment, that he had become almost human?

'It's all right, Ann. She's here,' she called loudly, as they neared the schoolroom. Ann appeared from round the back, brushing a damp tendril from her forehead. 'Oh, thank – oh, Gavin! You found her. Good for you. Right, children.' Then she saw Jane, and stared.

'What on earth—' she began.

Gavin said smoothly: 'I think a little first-aid is needed.' He swung Melanie down. 'Go on, you little minx, and don't run off again or I'll paddle your behind.' Melanie jumped away giggling, and ran to join her admiring companions.

Jane stood perfectly still, fighting the feeling of faintness that had suddenly overcome her. Ann went to her and took her arm.

'Sit down inside, I'll go and get some cold water. You've gone quite white.'

Silently Jane obeyed. She had no choice, even with him there, for she knew she couldn't remain standing much longer, with the pain causing such a sick sensation.

She heard Ann call something to Gavin, but barely heard the words, and the next moment found herself sitting on one of the dwarf-sized chairs.

'Phew!' Ann gave a sympathetic grimace. 'Your ankle's come up like a balloon!'

Jane managed a faint smile. 'Thanks – you make me feel much better – ouch!' This as Ann knelt to touch the swollen skin.

'You know, we ought to get Mac to look at this,' and as she said it, a shadow fell across the entrance, and Gavin walked in. Ann turned to him. 'Don't you think so?' she asked him.

He crouched down in front of Jane, then looked up. 'Yes, I do,' he agreed. 'But he won't be here for a while. I'll bandage it for now. Where's the first-aid box kept, Ann?'

'I'll get it.' She vanished into the small stockroom, and Gavin said softly: 'Why didn't you admit it hurt when I asked you? It must have been giving you hell.'

'I'm not asking for sympathy,' she answered shortly, wishing he would go away.

His mouth compressed. 'I didn't say you were. But I wish you weren't so—' Jane never knew what he had been about to say, for Ann came back carrying a large biscuit tin and a water jug.

Gavin's hands were deft and quick, and they watched him bandage Jane's ankle with cool efficiency. Jane's feelings were mixed. Relief as the cold wet bandage soothed, dismay at the churning sensation inside her caused by his touch.

'Thank you,' she said stiffly when he had finished and stood up.

'A pleasure.' He bowed slightly – mockingly. 'I'd better take you home, hadn't I?'

'No!' Realizing how sharply she had spoken, she added more gently: 'No, thanks, I'll tell the children a story – I can sit down for that.'

He shrugged. 'As you wish, Jane. Well,' he glanced at his watch, 'only an hour to go.'

Heavens, I must give the children their milk!' Ann clapped her hand to her mouth in dismay. Gavin glanced at Jane. 'As your assistant is out of action, I'll help.' And so saying, he vanished with her out of the doorway. Jane moved her chair so that she could keep an eye on the children – especially Melanie, who, perhaps because of Gavin's threat, was now keeping out of mischief as she dug with a little spade in the sand pit.

They came back with a jug of iced coffee as well as the large pitcher of milk, and after serving the children, who lined up obediently on Gavin's instructions, Jane and Ann sat down together and drank the icy sweet drink. Gavin stayed outside, and Ann whispered: 'He's marvellous with the children, you know. They'll do anything for him.'

Looking at them now, quietly handing him their empty beakers, Jane couldn't help but agree. But some imp of devilment drove her to say: 'Perhaps he terrifies them into obedience.' She regretted it immediately, but Ann laughed.

'I don't think so!' she said. 'He's different when he comes here from what he is at work, you know. More relaxed. No, I think he's one of those men who're not frightened to show a little gentleness occasionally. So many of them seem to think it's unmanly, don't they? But Gavin doesn't really give a damn what anyone thinks about him.'

Jane sipped her drink slowly. Something inside her longed to agree with Ann, but another part resisted the other's words. She didn't want to know about another side of him. She really *didn't* want to know. But she found herself watching him all the same, as he crouched down to answer a question from one of the children, his face serious, intent on what the other had to say, no trace of that usual arrogance in his face.

'Does he often come here?' Jane asked, very casually.

'Well,' Ann frowned, 'he's usually got too much to do to stay long. But—' she shrugged, 'you know him. He's unpredictable.'

In the extreme, added Jane inwardly. And she wondered, not for the first time that day, if Sara ever came to help out at the school. Now was not the time to ask, for Gavin was coming in carrying a pile of beakers, which he took to the sink in the corner.

'I'll have this compound fenced off,' he told Ann. 'Do any of the others take it into their heads to wander off like Melanie?'

'No. Not yet – but a fence would be a good idea,' Ann answered him. 'It would make our job easier.'

'I'll have it done tomorrow.' He glanced briefly at his watch. 'In fact, I'll go and arrange something about it now. Won't be long.'

'That's Gavin.' Ann shook her head. 'No sooner said than done. I'm almost sorry I won't be here tomorrow to see him in action.'

They didn't even have to wait that long, as it happened. A quarter of an hour later he returned with two of the islanders carrying spades and a mallet. The two women saw him pointing to various spots, then marking with sticks in the sandy soil of the clearing, watched by a fascinated audience of small children. Then he came in to them.

'I've phoned town from the factory office. There'll be a lorry coming with fencing, and posts, and cement in half an hour. Meanwhile we'll begin digging foundations for the posts. Keep the kids out of our way, will you, please

With a lithe, completely unselfconscious movement, he lifted off his shirt and flung it over the back of a chair. A pulse beat furiously in Jane's throat as she saw him stripped to the waist. Ann seemed quite unconcerned, and Jane swallowed hard, trying not to notice him – but that was impossible. Gavin was superbly built, his shoulders heavy and well muscled, his chest broad, darkly covered with black hair. A small medallion glinted silver as he moved, turning away to go outside, and Jane looked quickly down at her hands. She told herself firmly that it was perfectly natural for him to work like this; the men outside wore only shorts, and were bare-footed. But the odd sensation persisted, and it was almost a relief when Ann said, with a little amused laugh:

'My, but he's a well built fellow! No wonder half the girls on the island are after him!'

Jane cleared her throat. 'Oh, really?' she tried a laugh. 'But he's already – er – spoken for, isn't he?'

'Sara? Mmm, I suppose she's in the lead at the moment. She'd certainly like to be. But our Gavin's a wily bird. You've not met Kay yet?'

'No,' Jane shook her head. 'Unless she was at Sara's party last week?'

'Heavens, no! They don't even speak to one another – for obvious reasons, I might add! Kay will be at Shirley's

146

wedding, so you'll meet her there. Of course, Sara's coming too.' She pulled a little face. 'But I'll try and keep them well apart. Kay might not have a pushing momma like Leonie, but she has a lot going for her – as you'll see when you meet her.'

'I hope my ankle's all right by then,' Jane said, wondering why, quite suddenly, she didn't really want to go to the wedding after all.

She looked outside to where Gavin had already begun digging. It was interesting to watch, for he worked with an economy of movement that bespoke practice. Sweat glistened on his broad back as the spade lifted and fell, and sandy soil grew in a neat pile beside him.

'I wonder why he does this himself,' Jane said. 'Surely the other two would manage?'

Ann nodded. 'He enjoys the exercise, I imagine. And the men work far better when their "boss man" shows he can do it just as well. Besides—' she hesitated, and gave a little smile, 'he used to be very athletic, before his father died and he had to take on all his extra responsibilities. I suppose he likes to keep in trim – and, let's face it, this is as good a way as any.'

Jane remembered something, and said: 'Mac told me he was good in a fight too, but he didn't say why.'

Ann began to laugh. 'Oh, *that*! Oh, dear, it was all over the island at the time. It's several years ago now, actually, but I suppose Mac's not forgotten – I wonder if Gavin has?' she gave a faint, reminiscent smile, and Jane, agog, whispered:

'But what happened?'

'Oh, well, it was just after he'd taken over the factories, after his father died. There was some trouble between the men, and it developed into a fight – I think some of them had been drinking – anyway, Mac and Gavin happened to arrive just as things were in full swing – punches being exchanged, bodies littering the floor – a real roundhouse, Mac said. Gavin took one look, decided which were the two ringleaders – there usually are in a fight, aren't there?' Jane nodded, dying of curiosity, and unwilling to interrupt Ann. 'And then he waded in with fists flying, and had both of them out cold in a matter of seconds – after that, it sort of petered out. Mac said it was a joy to see – but I'm not so sure,' she shuddered. 'I'm glad *I* wasn't there.'

'Yes, me too,' Jane answered. But her eyes were on Gavin, quite unaware that he was being talked about. She had sensed his strength and power when they had first met. Now, reluctant admiration for his undoubted courage filled her. She heard Ann say something about fetching a drink for the men, and nodded, scarcely noticing. The many facets of Gavin's personality were puzzling and disquieting. Every day, it seemed, she learned something new about him, and all the things she heard went into making the picture of a man whose character had unknown depths, who had a strange magnetism that frightened her by its intensity. He was undoubtedly the central figure on the island; a man who, in some way, touched and affected the lives of all those around him. Jane stood, suddenly restless, and walked slowly and carefully to the door. There, aware that Gavin's eyes were on her, she paused, suddenly shy, about to go back – until Melanie cried out: 'Jane, look what I've done!'

Smiling, relieved, she went over to the sand pit to see the castle the children were building. There she bent down to admire it. And at that moment a hooter sounded in the distance and she looked up.

'That's for the mothers to come and collect their offspring,' Gavin missed nothing, she thought. He stuck

148

the spade in the hard soil and walked over to her. 'Your day is over. Are you glad?'

Jane looked up sharply. 'I've enjoyed it,' she answered.

'Think you'll come again?' he countered swiftly.

'Yes. Why didn't you tell me it was all yours?' she asked.

He smiled crookedly. 'Ah, you know?'

'Yes.' She struggled awkwardly to her feet, and his hand was suddenly on her arm, but it disturbed her, so that she moved slightly away, still looking at him.

'Well,' he seemed amused, 'I thought you might not offer if you knew.' He looked away, his eye caught by Ann returning with jug and beakers. 'Would you have?' he added softly.

'I don't know.' Jane was wishing that she hadn't spoken so hastily.

'There you are, then.' He suddenly cocked his head. 'I can hear something. It's either the bus or the stuff for the fence. Excuse me.' He strode off towards the road, and Ann came up. 'Where's he gone now?'

'To see what's arrived,' Jane answered.

'Oh. He'll have to have his drink when he comes back. You want one, Jane?'

'No, thanks, it doesn't matter. I think Mac will be coming to take me home soon.'

And even as she spoke, Mac appeared, with a crowd of chattering, brightly clothed women, who waved and called to their children as they neared the clearing. Within minutes each child had been paired off with its mother, and gone, and there was silence.

Ann looked round her. 'Well, Mac, another day gone. Jane's done very well.'

'I knew she would. And what have you been doing, young lady?' he gave her a frowning glance.

'I was chasing Melanie, and I tripped,' Jane told him
'Hmm, seems to be bandaged properly. I'll check it when you get home. Ready to go, Jane?'

'Yes.' She turned to Ann. 'Thank you for showing me the ropes. I've enjoyed my day. Will I see you before the wedding?'

'I hope so. I come here again on Thursday. Perhaps . . .' she stopped and smiled a little smile.

'I'll try,' promised Jane. 'Goodbye.'

She and Mac walked slowly away from the school, and Ann turned away, after waving, and began to pick up abandoned toys. Jane sighed. The two labourers were still digging. Of Gavin there was no sign. Then, as they reached Mac's car, they saw him standing talking to a lorry driver parked just off the road. The bus was drawing away in the distance.

Gavin turned, saw them, said something to the driver who jumped in his cab and started to back, very slowly, and then he came over to them.

'The stuff's arrived for the fence,' he said. 'He's taking it round the other way, it's quicker.' Then he looked at Jane. 'Thanks for coming,' he said quietly. 'I appreciate your help.' His words were just for her. Mac might not have been there. And just for an instant, a precious instant, Jane saw something in his eyes that made her go warm inside.

The moment passed, goodbyes were said, and she got into Mac's car. Gavin held the door open for her, then began talking to Mac, the other side. She heard their voices, but the words didn't register. There was only the memory of his eyes, as they had been when he had looked at her. Dark eyes, fathomless. Jane tightened her grip on her bag. Suddenly she wanted to cry, but she couldn't for the life of her have said why.

CHAPTER EIGHT

THE next two days passed very slowly. The heat was intense, and Jane put her lack of appetite down to that, plus the fact that her ankle was sore in the heat. Mac had given her some special lotion which she had to rub in twice a day, and which did much to reduce the swelling.

The wedding approached, and Jane wondered whether she would go. On Wednesday, in the early evening, she asked her father. They were sitting out at the end of the garden, within sight of the sea, and the air was cool with a refreshing breeze that had sprung up. Megan and Colin were coming for supper later, and Jane had already decided to be extra nice to him. She liked him, and she knew that he was attracted to her, a knowledge that only a few short days ago would have filled her with pleasurable delight. Now, for some odd reason, she wished he wasn't. She couldn't explain, or rationalize her feelings; she didn't understand them. And she wondered why Gavin had not been to see her father since Sunday. Of course, she thought, I don't *care*, but he might have been to see if my ankle was better. But he hadn't, and somehow, ever so slightly, of course, it nagged at her mind. To rid herself of such disquieting thoughts, she said: 'Will you be going to Shirley's wedding on Saturday, Father?'

'Now you're here, yes, I think I will. I wasn't too sure before, Jane, but I'll make the effort. It'll do me good. We'll ask Megan if we can go with them I think – ah, here they are.'

'Hello, John, Jane,' Megan was coming across the lawn

from the house, followed by Colin, dressed in black slacks and thin white sweater, accentuating his tall leanness. 'Hello, Jane, Mr. Ritchie,' he squatted down beside Jane's chair. 'I heard about your ankle. Is it any better?'

'Lots.' She smiled at him, wondering who had told him. Gavin? 'We were just talking about Shirley's wedding.'

'You're going?' he asked eagerly.

Her father's voice cut in: 'We're hoping to. We're also hoping that some very good friends of ours might offer to run us there.'

'Why of course, we'd be delighted,' Megan answered. 'And you're already learning to drive, Jane. How do you like it?'

'I – it was better than I thought,' Jane answered with a smile. 'Gavin offered to teach me on Sunday afternoon, and we went to the airport.'

'I know – Mac told me.' Megan gave Jane a secret look. 'Was he very fierce?'

'No,' Jane laughed. But inwardly she cried: if only you knew! 'No, he was quite patient. I hadn't a clue at first, but found it easier after a while. Very tiring, though.'

'Mmm. Well, any time you want a lesson, just ask. Of course you'll have to wait a few days, until that ankle's stronger.' She became more brisk. 'Now, the wedding. You'll go with us. What about a dress, Jane?'

Jane looked at her in sudden dismay. 'Oh, I hadn't thought—'

'No problem,' her father interrupted. 'You can go and buy something—'

'But I couldn't—' Jane began, as Megan also said:

'I know, let's make you one – in Saramanca lace.'

There was silence, and all eyes were turned to Megan, who laughed 'Heavens, what have I said?'

'But you couldn't. It would take ages!' Jane protested.

'Nonsense! It's Wednesday today. We'll buy the stuff tomorrow, and I'll have it made by Friday. Good gracious, I've not much else to do. I'd *love* to, honestly!'

Jane's father looked at her with affection. 'There you are, then! Megan's sewing is famous, I can vouch for that.'

'It's very kind of you,' Jane said hesitantly. 'Are you sure—'

'I'm sure. There, that's settled. Tomorrow morning I'll take you to town, and we'll buy the lace and something to go under it from Gavin's—'

'Somebody talking about me?' a voice came from nearby, and they all turned to see Gavin and Carlo approaching from the direction of his garden. Jane's first, absurd thought was: Why does he have to turn up when the others are here? That was followed by an awful panicky feeling she didn't understand. She wanted to run away somewhere – anywhere away from him. But she must not. She must remain, and talk, and hope that he would go away soon.

Megan began to explain what they had been saying, and Jane felt Colin's silent withdrawal from beside her as he went for another chair. Carlo flopped down in his place and pushed a damp nose to nuzzle Jane's hand. She stroked his head, watching him but listening to Gavin, hearing him say: 'And I'd come to ask Jane a favour! I can hardly do that now.'

'What was it?' Her voice was casual, deceptively so, for inside she quivered.

'Ann's on her own tomorrow, at the school, and she wondered if you felt well enough to go,' he said.

So that was why he had come! She should have known! She looked at Megan, not knowing what to say, and Megan laughed. 'Trust you!' she turned a smiling face to Jane. 'It's up to you, love. I'll get the materials if you like – just let me take your measurements before I go, to give me an idea how much we'll need, and I can—'

'I'll take Jane to the store at eight, Megan, and she can look round. That's if you're going, Jane?'

'All right, of course I'll help.' She was dimly aware of Colin moving uneasily near her, but it didn't seem important. 'I just don't want to put Megan out, that's all.'

'Heavens, you're not doing that. I've got to go anyway, later on. I'll collect what you choose, and then we'll get together when you come home and start cutting out.'

Jane felt as if her life was being decided for her. They all watched her, waiting for her decision. She nodded. 'All right. Thank you, Megan.'

Afterwards, much later, when she lay in bed, she thought wryly how it seemed that Gavin always got his own way. It had happened so naturally, but now, analysing it, she realized just how easily he had managed it. Everyone seemed only too eager to fall in with *his* plans. *Everyone.* Why, oh, why was it? How did he do it? Restlessly she turned in bed, the thought uppermost in her mind that he was taking her to the store – *his* store – and then on to the school. And she had meekly agreed. She began to wonder why, when she had already decided to have as little as possible to do with him. It was as if she was being drawn, irresistibly, into the circle of power that he so effortlessly commanded.

Eventually she slept, and the face she saw before sleep claimed her was Gavin's, as he had looked in the clearing when he was about to pick Melanie up in his arms. He had looked so very different then, so very different.

She left the bandage off for the first time the next

morning, dismayed to see a paler patch where it had been. As she dressed and brushed her hair, she realized that she had only been on Saramanca for just over a week. It seemed unbelievable. She felt as if she had lived there for ages, almost as if the island were now a part of her. Soon she would have to make a choice – and she wasn't sure yet what it would be. One part of her wanted very much to remain with her father, another gave her pause; some deep instinct of self-preservation that told her she should get away, before it was too late – but too late for what? That she did not, could not, guess at.

Her father was up early, his face seeming more relaxed and healthy than she had seen before. He greeted her as she went down to breakfast.

'I think I'll go for a walk today,' he said. 'I'm feeling better than I have done for a long time.'

A guilty pang shot through Jane. 'Shall I stay – and come with you?' she asked.

He laughed. 'No, they need you at the school – and I'm so glad you're going, Jane. You are truly my daughter – I'm proud of you, offering to help like you did. Very proud.'

Jane didn't know what to say. His words, so quietly and sincerely spoken, brought a lump to her throat. Every day she grew more to love this gentle man, her father, and every day the bitterness of the wasted years faded a little more. Perhaps it was fate that they should not have been reunited before. Perhaps now was the best time – the right time for it to have happened. She put her hand on his. 'I can see a difference in you, Father. You look so much better than when I came. I'm glad, really glad.'

'It's your doing, Jane. I have something to live for now. Someone to call my own. You are just as I would have wished you to be.'

'Thank you.' Emotion choked her so that she could eat no more. She pushed her plate away. 'I – I'd better get ready for Gavin. He'll be here in a minute.'

She fled upstairs to the sanctuary of her room, blinking back the tears desperately. It would be awful if Gavin should see her like this!

When she heard the knock she was sufficiently composed, after splashing her face with cold water, to go down and let him in herself.

'I won't be a moment,' she told him. 'I'll just say goodbye to my father.'

Driving towards Port Patrick, he looked at her curiously. But all he said was: 'Is your ankle better?'

'Yes, thank you.' The odd feeling she had experienced in the clearing with him on Monday seemed to have vanished, and she felt uneasy and almost tense again. He seemed to sense it, and spoke about the school, about the trouble they had had putting up the fence, in a completely impersonal tone, as if he were talking to a stranger he had just met. He looked dynamically attractive, dressed simply in a fine silk shirt that was laced instead of buttoned at the front, and matching fawn slacks. Jane remembered Ann's words. So half the girls on the island were after him, were they? She was glad that she wasn't one of them. She could imagine just how unbearable he could be if he imagined for one minute – but what had he thought the other night, after the party? Jane went warm as the memory she tried so hard to erase rushed back. Oh yes, undoubtedly he had thought she was flinging herself at him. And – the idea came suddenly, awfully – was that why he had asked her to go and help in the school? Did he perhaps hope . . . Jane stiffened in her seat as a dreadful thought invaded her head. She had no illusions about men – especially sophisticated, experienced men in their thirties, as Gavin undoubtedly was. Aunt Dorothy had taken a constant delight in warning her that they were all the same – 'only out for what they can get'. And Gavin was a man – very much so – so he was no different from the others and very probably worse. He had been used to getting his own way nearly all his life. He knew he was attractive – he'd be stupid if he didn't, and he was very far from stupid. Of course, Jane thought. I should have realized! He hates me – and yet sometimes he looks at me in a certain way, and the touch of his hand on my arm – all little things that hadn't meant much at the time they had happened came rushing back to her. Perhaps he had been assessing her, *weighing up* the chance . . .

'Anything the matter?'

She jerked round sharply. 'No – no.' But her eyes couldn't meet his, fearful that he would read her thoughts.

'Oh.' He seemed amused, almost laughing – as if he *knew*.

What a fool she was! Jane moved uneasily in her seat, wishing she hadn't come with him. She should have refused. She should have—

'You've gone very quiet.'

'I was thinking,' she answered. Her quickened heart-beats slowed down; she must keep calm, must not give herself away – for what hope was there for her *then*? 'We're nearly there, aren't we?'

'We are indeed.' His hand tightened on the wheel as he swerved slightly to avoid a cat that darted out from no-where on to the road. A few minutes later he was pulling into the car park behind the shop. Everything was quiet and deserted, and he opened the back door with a key. It was only when they were in the close confines of the lift that she was able to ask, very casually: 'What time does the store open?'

'Nine-thirty today. You can look round in peace.'

That wasn't what she had meant. Jane brushed away a stupid fluttery feeling inside her, but even so, she was glad when the lift stopped, and he led the way through the dress department, ghostly and quiet with shrouded models standing like captured spirits waiting only to be set free. Gavin went through an archway, touched a panel of switches, and fluorescent lights flickered and came to life. And all was so silent that Jane feared to breathe.

'Look around. I'll get some lace down first.' Gavin shattered the stillness as he moved, and Jane wandered around slowly, marvelling at the shelves which stretched from floor to ceiling full of bales of multi-coloured materials.

'I'll be spoilt for choice,' she admitted, after a few moments, and it wasn't quite so bad now, for he was occupied in looking round too.

He laughed. 'I know. Let me help. I've a good idea what you want.' He indicated some lace. 'Have a look at that. What colour would you like under it? Pink – blue – yellow?'

He lifted down bale after bale of wild silk in exquisite, exotic colours that almost shimmered in the high overhead lights. 'Wait,' Jane said. 'That yellow. May I see it together with the lace?' The lace was gossamer fine, cobweb delicate, and off white, almost old ivory, in shade. The shimmering yellow silk he slid underneath it on the counter set it off to perfection, and Jane breathed deeply. 'This, I think. Yes.'

'Then try it against you. Here, at this mirror. Stand still.'

As Jane crossed to the bevelled glass on a stand, enabling it to be swivelled at any angle, she watched him lift

158

the rolls of silk and lace, and she wondered ...

'Now, hold that.' He spun a length of silk from the roll, and held it up for her to take, and Jane had an oddly breathless sensation in her chest. 'Put it against you.' Wordlessly she obeyed. And now there was a tight band, suffocating her because he was very near now. He bent and carefully unwound the exquisite soft lace from its bale.

'Be careful,' she began. 'You mustn't—'

'I know what I'm doing.' His voice was quiet, strangely so, as if he too ... Jane's heartbeat was loud. She could feel it thudding against her ribs as he straightened, and with infinite care, lifted the lace to her. Then his hands were at her neck and waist as he eased it round her. There was something almost impersonal about his touch – almost, but even so she felt stifled, panicky, as if she needed to get away. She stirred uneasily, and he said: 'Stand still. Look at yourself.' She saw their reflections in the mirror, Gavin behind her with his hands on her shoulders, the beautiful material sweeping down, looking very like an evening dress. But it wasn't that she found herself watching, it was him. He was so near that she could feel the warmth of his body, smell the clean male scent of aftershave lotion, and her throat became constricted so that her voice came out as a croak. 'Th-this is lovely. I think I'll—'

'Yes, it is.' Something in his voice made her tingle inside, and she wanted him to go. She half turned, eyes wide, and he moved so that the lace slid down slightly. 'I'm sorry,' he said, and caught it. His hand, just for a split second of time, brushed against her breast, and he moved it sharply away. Turning, he said: 'Right, I'll have it put away for Megan. She'll know how many yards.' But his voice was almost husky, as though he had been running.

'Yes, thank you.' Jane couldn't look at him. Her head felt as if it would burst with the tension that had suddenly, indefinably sprung up between them. He swept up the bundles of material and threw them on the counter.

'Are you ready to go?' He sounded impatient, almost harsh.

'Yes.' She picked up her bag, heard him jingle the keys in his pocket, and walked quickly out ahead of him to the lift.

He jabbed the button and they travelled down in silence. There was an oddness about his manner that disturbed her – almost as if he were angry. But what had she done? Jane swallowed hard, felt the lift stop with a slight bump, and went out quickly towards the outer door, leaving Gavin to close the lift door and follow. She felt she had to say something, anything, to dispel the brittle atmosphere, and as she stepped outside into the hot sunlight, she said: 'Thank you for bringing me. W-will I need a hat on Saturday?'

He paused in the act of locking the door and looked at her. 'Yes. Do you want to go back and try some on now?'

'No,' she shook her head. 'No, it can wait.' His jaw muscles tightened.

'Right. Let's go.' He locked the door and they went to the car. As they drove to the school, Jane's head began to ache, a dull throbbing that wasn't helped by the sun's glare. She didn't know what had caused it, but the tension that existed in the car was unbearable. There was nothing she could do about it, for Gavin seemed to have retreated into a world of his own, driving swiftly along, his face looking ahead, never once glancing at her. Jane's fingers tightened on her bag miserably. She should never have agreed to come with him. Oh, if only she could drive properly! The sooner she learned the better. And the sooner they arrived at the school the better too. She put a hand to her burning forehead to try and hold back the throb of pain, and he looked at her.

'What's the matter?' It was the voice of a stranger, remote and unfriendly.

Something snapped inside Jane. She had done nothing – why should *she* feel guilty? 'I've got a splitting head-ache,' she answered. 'But please don't let it worry *you*. It'll pass.'

'Not in this heat it won't. There are aspirins at the school. Ann will get a couple if you remind me to ask her.'

'I can ask her myself,' she said quickly. 'If you'll just drop me off there—'

'Are you sure? I can come in – but I have rather a lot to do today—'

'Quite sure.'

'I'll collect you at four, of course.'

'Mac can do that,' she said swiftly.

'No, he's got a maternity case in town. A woman who always has difficulty, so he's staying there today.'

'I see.' Jane's mouth tightened rebelliously. It seemed as if he was regretting having brought her. But why? She was doing him the favour after all. 'It's a pity I can't drive myself, isn't it?' something made her say. 'Then you wouldn't have to go out of your way for me.'

'I'm glad of your help. It's no trouble to me, I assure you.'

'Really?' she turned away and looked out at the countryside racing past them. There was a tight knot of pain in her chest that refused to go away, and when he began to slow down preparatory to stopping at the entrance to the school, she touched the handle. Even before he had finally stopped, she pushed the door open. 'Goodbye.' Without looking back, she got out and slammed the door behind her and walked away. She heard the engine thrum into life, heard him turning the car, then a toot of the horn – but she would not, *could* not look back. Then the sound faded into the distance, and she paused to collect her breath and rest her ankle, leaning for a moment against the trunk of a gnarled old tree. Jane didn't understand why she felt as she did, only that for some absurd reason she wanted to cry. Taking a deep breath, she began walking again, and heard the voices of the children as she neared the school. Here was normality, here she could be herself. For of one thing she was sure – she couldn't be with Gavin.

The day passed swiftly, and in between supervising the children, a job made much easier by the presence of the high fence stretching round their playground, Ann and Jane discussed the coming wedding. It seemed that most of the island would be there. Shirley was marrying an Australian she had met on holiday two years previously, and was going to live in Perth after the honeymoon. Ann brought out photos of her daughter, a pretty girl with a friendly face, looking like a younger version of her mother. Jane handed back the snaps with a smile. 'She looks a lovely girl,' she remarked

'She is, although I shouldn't say so. You'd get on fine with her, Jane. It's a pity she's leaving on Saturday. If only you'd come a few months ago!'

And somehow Jane found herself telling Ann about her reasons for coming now – and not before. The older woman heard her story in silence, a growing dismay on her face as the tale unfolded. When Jane had finished, she exclaimed: 'How wicked! But how marvellous that you should find out when you did! Oh, Jane, I'm so glad to know you found out eventually. Everyone says how different your father's been since you came. I'm sure you're doing him a world of good.'

'I hope so,' Jane smiled slightly. 'Mac wants me to persuade him to see a specialist. I'm waiting for the right moment to broach the subject.'

'You do,' Ann nodded. 'He will for you, I'm sure. Why, you've given him a purpose in life again.'

And once more Jane found herself thinking about her father's plea for her to stay. As each day passed, she realized more and more that she belonged with him. She would find a way to repay Aunt Dorothy, even if it meant taking a job – for this was one thing she would do alone, without her father's help. Only then would she feel free of the guilt that still plagued her about leaving her aunt alone. She asked Ann, while the thought was still fresh in her mind: 'Are there any jobs on the island that I could do?'

'Why? Whatever for?' Ann looked so startled that Jane felt obliged to explain.

'But surely your father would—'

'No.' Jane shook her head decisively. 'It's something I must do alone – I – I can't explain why.'

Ann patted her arm. 'I do understand. Really. And I admire your independence. I'm sure your father will too. But weren't you going to train to be a teacher?'

'Yes. But it's three years at college before I qualify. I'm willing to work in an office – anything really—' her voice tailed away at Ann's expression. 'Why, what is it?'

Ann laughed. 'Don't you *see*? Here! This school! Gavin's going to get it on a proper footing soon. Why not ask him if you can work here?'

Jane shook her head, unable to tell Ann the truth. 'I – don't know. I'll have to think about it.'

'Do. He'll have to get someone who's already trained, of course, as well, but you'd be ideal. You've already shown that on Monday. You like the children – and they certainly like you, and that's half the battle, believe me!'

Jane traced a pattern on the table with her forefinger. If the school had been Mac's alone, and he in charge, she wouldn't have hesitated. But it wasn't. It was Gavin's – and that made all the difference. All the difference in the world.

The day of the wedding dawned, and Jane was up early to go over to Megan's house for the final touches to be put to her dress. The two of them had cut it out and tacked it on Thursday evening, and Friday morning Jane had walked over to Megan's house to watch, and help in the sewing.

Megan's home was similar to John's, roomy and white, with cool furnishings and rugs, flowers in every room, and the warmer touches of a woman's occupation. Jane had sat watching Megan busily sewing at the electric Singer, the floor littered with scraps of lace and gleaming silk, as her busy fingers guided the delicate fabric under the needle.

They got on well, and Jane cooked lunch for them both in the large kitchen at noon. Afterwards they rested and drank fresh pineapple juice as the noonday sun reached its height.

Now, Saturday, Jane ate breakfast and set off to walk to Megan's. There was virtually nothing to do now, except any last-minute stitches that might be needed after the final fitting.

'Hello,' Megan opened the door wide. 'Come in, Jane. You've just missed Colin. He went early to the store today, with the wedding being this afternoon. Oh, it's so hot, isn't it?' She led the way into her sewing room and Jane gasped at the sight of the dress hanging up on the tall cupboard.

'Why, Megan, it's lovely!' she exclaimed.

'Let's try it on – then I'll show you my collection of hats! I never wear one except at weddings, and I've several, nearly new.'

Jane sighed. 'How on earth can I ever repay you for all you've done?' she asked.

Megan laughed. 'Just pretend I'm your fairy god-mother! I've already told you, I *like* doing things. And a fat chance I get with my son. What can you make for a man, tell me that?'

Both laughing now, they began the final trying on session.

Jane hadn't seen the island church, but she had vaguely imagined something typically English. It was therefore a surprise as they turned into a wide tree-lined drive, already full of cars, to see the simple white building with its sloping green pantiled roof shimmering in the heat. Bells clamoured vigorously in the square bell tower at one end. Jane glanced at her father sitting beside her in the back, worried lest he should feel tired or ill. He caught her glance and smiled. 'I'm fine,' he whispered, as if guessing her thoughts by her face.

Colin turned round as he stopped. 'Everybody all right?'

'Yes, thanks.' But Jane had an unaccountably shy feeling as they all stepped out. It was one thing to look at yourself in a mirror and feel good, quite another to face dozens of strangers, all looking extremely smart and assured. She was introduced by Megan to lots of people, and felt the ripple of surprise that went round as they saw her father. She felt very much aware of everything, quite suddenly; as if all her senses were finally attuned to all that was going on around her. She did not know why, nor did she know that soon, very soon, she would make the most momentous discovery of her life. After which everything would be changed. And with each moment that passed, the discovery drew nearer, but Jane was unaware of this instant of destiny to come, and she talked, and smiled shyly as she met the men and women who were friends of the Murrays, and in a quiet corner, where she and Megan had escaped for a breather, Jane asked curiously: 'Who's that girl over there?' She pointed to a strikingly beautiful dark-haired girl who stood slightly aloof from the others, talking to an elderly woman.

Megan looked. 'That's Kay Wallace. Isn't she stunning? And a nice girl too. I'll introduce you later. She's very friendly with Gavin.' So that was the one Ann had spoken of! Jane had a sharp pain inside her – but still she didn't know, didn't realize. The moment had not yet arrived.

There was a stir of movement, and the crowd began to break up as people drifted into the church in ones and twos. The chatter diminished as they entered the cool interior, and the sound of the organ swelled forth to greet them. Jane had not yet seen Gavin, and had wondered why. Perhaps he would be late. What did it matter? She looked round at the cream walls, dark ceiling beams, and the simple altar with a plain gold cross in front of a stained glass window through which the sun filtered in glittering reds and blues and yellows. Two men sat alone and apart at the front, one a stranger, the other with a disturbingly familiar back.

Of course, thought Jane. I should have known – Gavin is the best man. He turned slightly to speak to his companion, his profile etched sharply against the cream background. He was wearing a pearly grey jacket, immaculate white shirt, and he looked darkly handsome, almost a stranger. Jane's heart lurched, and she turned quickly away, fearful to be caught staring, especially by Colin, who sat beside her. Her glance travelled over and rested on Kay, who was looking in Gavin's direction, her beautiful classical features perfectly calm and composed. Yet even from the distance, there was something disturbing in her expression as her eyes rested on the man in the front pew.

The next moment the organ struck up the age-old, familiar strains of: 'Here Comes the Bride', and the congregation rose as one. All eyes turned to the bride, walking towards her groom, her arm in her father's. There was something so moving about the marriage service, thought Jane, even when they were, to her, comparative strangers. And as it proceeded, and everyone there witnessed the simple ceremony, she found her eyes, not on the couple, but on Gavin. He had not once looked back, hadn't seen her, yet Jane had the strangest feeling, as if he were strongly aware – as if he *knew* she were looking. And then, minutes later, it happened. It was the end of the service, and the newlywedded couple were about to go into the vestry to sign the register; there was a momentary confusion with the young bridesmaids, and Gavin turned, just for a few seconds, and his eyes met Jane's. He hadn't looked round before. It was as if he had known exactly where she was sitting. Dark, his eyes, shadowed with that distance between, but there might have been no one else in that church, for those few moments. And she looked away, shaken and confused, almost light-headed, unable to *bear* it any longer. For she knew now, with a dizzy spiral of self-realization bursting inside her, knew that she loved Gavin Grant.

They drove to the reception at the Murrays' afterwards, and Jane chatted to Colin and her father, and Megan, and hoped desperately that nothing of the shattering knowledge showed in her face. Gavin had come over to talk to them, and she felt the tight knot of misery grow inside her, for with him was Kay, and her slim hand rested gently on his arm, just the lightest butterfly touch as she smiled at Jane, and admired her dress. From somewhere inside her Jane found the courage to smile back and talk normally, and was glad of Colin, tall and handsome at her side, his arm lightly round her as the four of them talked. Jane could not meet Gavin's eyes. She watched Kay instead, admiring the cool dark beauty of her face, with its serene expression, and the thickly lashed eyes that surveyed her in such a genuinely friendly way. Here was none of Sara's bitchiness – but something else instead, a supreme confidence in herself that made Jane feel like a leggy schoolgirl. Jane could not know just how young and appealing she herself looked, how exquisitely the dress fitted her, or that her very shyness was lending her a beauty unequalled in that large marquee. Gently and quietly she answered Kay's questions about how she liked the island, and was it what she had expected? And when Gavin at last added his own contribution, about her days at the school, she was able to look at him.

'I do find it interesting, yes,' she said. 'And not as hard as I thought it might be.' His cool grey eyes met hers, and she tilted her chin defiantly. He didn't *know*. Heaven forbid that he ever should! If she could only act *normally!*

'I'd like a word with you about it, actually,' he said. 'But perhaps not here. I've had a chat with Ann Murray.'

Jane's heart skipped a beat. What had Ann said? Oh, what a fool I was, she thought suddenly, not to have warned her not to say anything. She managed to smile. 'Really? Perhaps later. Will you excuse me, I must go and see if my father wants anything?'

'Surely,' Gavin nodded; Kay smiled, and Jane turned away, followed by Colin as she made her escape.

He took her arm. 'Say, what's up with you and Gavin?' he whispered fiercely as they went outside on to the lawn, no less hot than the interior of the marquee.

'What – what do you mean?' she asked in alarm.

He shrugged. 'I don't honestly know! Just this odd feeling I get whenever you two are together, like—' he searched for words, '—like invisible sparks flying about.' He gave a mock shiver. 'Boy, you could cut the atmosphere with a knife! And I don't just mean today. I've noticed it before.'

'You've got a vivid imagination,' Jane rejoined swiftly, waving at her father who was sitting under a large shady tree with Megan and Mac. She must be more careful not to let her feelings show. If she gave herself away ... The result would be too awful to contemplate. With a very determined, almost desperate effort, she managed to say: 'We don't particularly like one another, that's all. It happens sometimes – you know, a clash of personalities?'

'Yes, but—' he began, then stopped as if thinking better of it.

He shrugged again. 'It's not important. As you say, it sometimes happens.' And he took her arm and they went over to join the others.

Later there was dancing on the lawn under the stars to

169

the soft muted strains of an orchestra played over loud-speakers from a record player. Jane couldn't help contrasting this evening with Sara's party, and how different the atmosphere was. Sara was at the reception, and Gavin seemed to be skilfully dividing his time between her and Kay. He's got everything, thought Jane wryly, as she whirled round in Colin's arms. Looks and wealth – and two attractive women in tow. Oh, yes, he was clever all right – and she had to fall for him, idiot that she was. The pain of seeing him dancing close to Kay was like a knife in her heart, and she tried desperately to relax in Colin's arms. If only she could feel a spark for him – if only ... But it was no use. He might have been a stranger. She sensed, too, a slight withdrawal in him – perhaps he guessed – but how could he?

Later she danced with Mac, and the news he gave her almost banished her misery – almost.

'I've been having a talk with your dad,' he said, during their dance. 'He's agreed to go to Ceylon to see a pal of mine, James Carruthers – and it's all your doing!'

'Mine? But I haven't got round to—' she began, bewildered. He laughed softly. 'No, but I've persuaded him to do it for *your* sake!'

'Oh, Mac, I'm so glad. When will he go?'

'Next week some time, perhaps Tuesday. I'll phone Jimmy tomorrow and fix it before your dad changes his mind. I'll go too – it's an excuse to get off work for a day or two!'

'Shall I come as well?' she asked. The music died away and they were left standing in a patch of shadow, away from the paper lanterns strung across the gardens from tree to tree. Mac rubbed his chin thoughtfully. 'Och, well, I don't know, Jane. You see, Gavin's taking us, and strictly speaking, his plane's only a small one – and besides, I think he wants you here.'

'Who – Gavin or my father?' But before he could answer, she saw the man she couldn't seem to avoid coming across the grass towards them. And this time he was alone.

Mac turned to him. 'I've told Jane about her father. Can she come with us?' Gavin looked silently at her, and Jane began to shiver, as if she had done something wrong. Then he spoke: 'Well, as a matter of fact someone has already asked me for a lift—' he stopped, and ran his fingers through his hair. For the first time ever, he seemed unsure of himself, and Jane had a tremor of apprehension. What was the matter? Who could the other passenger be?

'Look, Mac, can I have a word with Jane, alone?'

'Sure!' Mac looked amused, and half turned. 'See you.'

As he walked away, Gavin took Jane's arm and steered her towards the darker shadows of the trees. She instinctively resisted, not knowing why, and he said softly: 'I'm not going to *eat* you. I want to talk.'

'Y-you'll be missed, won't you?' she said desperately. 'B-besides, you can say what you have to say here.'

'All right,' his voice was neutral, without expression. 'Here will do as well as anywhere. At least let us sit down.' He indicated a bench under the nearest tree, and she went to it, glad of the chance to sit down before her legs failed her. He sat beside her and began:

'I'll put it straight to you. Ann told me you might want work—' at her gasp of dismay he held out his hand. 'All right, I'm sorry to put it like that. Let me phrase it another way. Would you consider going to the school regularly for a proper salary?' And without a change of expression, he added: 'You are going to stay on here, aren't you?'

Jane looked down at her hands, clasped in her lap. How could she do it *now*, knowing what she did about herself? She had had doubts before about working at the school – they were reinforced tenfold since she had realized that she was in love with Gavin.

'I don't know,' she said unhappily.

'What don't you know? Whether you're staying on, or whether you'll work at the school?'

She looked up then at the tone of his voice, and their eyes met. In the dim shadows his face was a grey blur, softened by the dark. Even so, his expression seemed grim. Jane's heart beat rapidly, his nearness overwhelming her. Oh, if he knew! How he would laugh! With lips that trembled, she said: 'Ann shouldn't have said anything. I didn't–' she stopped helplessly.

'You didn't make the suggestion, is that it?' his voice was harsh.

'No – yes, I mean, but it was only an – an idea. I can't–' she shook her head. 'I don't want to–' 'work for you,' she had been going to say, but the words wouldn't came out.

He gave a short humourless laugh, as if she had, as he answered: 'You don't mind doing it voluntarily, but you don't want to work for me – is that it?'

She swallowed hard. 'All right, since you put it so bluntly. No, I don't,' and she looked up in desperate challenge. His breathing was deep, she could see his chest moving, and with dismay, she knew he was angry.

'Thanks for being so frank.' His eyes were dark as he looked at her. 'May I ask why?'

'I don't know!' She couldn't look away, for his eyes held hers forcefully.

'Oh, yes, you do. What's the matter?' Contempt lashed

her. 'Scared to hurt my feelings? Come now, I hadn't noticed any particular reticence on your part before.'

At something in his voice, all Jane's nervousness went. Damn the man, she thought wildly. Why should *I* be frightened? Why should I be like everyone else? I've got nothing to lose now, I know that. He thinks I'm a child. Nothing, absolutely *nothing* could ever make him look at me the way he looks at Sara, or Kay. A thread of temper ran through her voice as she answered him. 'All right. I don't want to work for you because – because you think you can b-boss everybody about, and you're not going to boss me!' And then she stopped, appalled. What had she said? She had done it again!

'You must be joking – or mad! I "boss" everyone about, do I? Well, well, and I never knew!' Sarcasm iced his words, and Jane half stood. With a sudden movement he jerked her down. 'Sit down! I feel like bossing *you* about sometimes, I can tell you! Damn it all, why are you always fighting me?'

A sob caught in Jane's throat. He was almost funny! 'Fighting?' she gasped. 'Me? How can I fight you?'

'Very easily,' he answered grimly. 'In the usual feminine underhand way, I might add—'

'I'm not stopping here to be insulted by *you*,' she whispered back, her whole body a turmoil of mixed anger and weakness that threatened to overcome her. 'How *dare* you speak to me like that!' She stood up and stamped her foot, resisting the strong urge to kick him instead. 'Get back to your – your girl-friends, and I'll—'

'And you'll get back to your Colin.' He stood too, towering over her easily. 'You can't take it, can you? It's fine for you to hand out the insults, but you can't take them – oh, no, you get all outraged, and stamp your foot!' He laughed grimly. 'Why don't you slap my face? Give them all something to talk about.'

'Don't tempt me,' she gritted, but her glance flew uneasily to the house. Surely no one could overhear?

'No,' he mocked. 'Nobody's noticed – yet. But just keep on, you're doing fine.'

'I hate you!' she whispered. 'Do you hear me? I *hate* you!'

'Do you? Then let's see if you hate *this*.' And suddenly she was swept against him and his arms went around her in a powerful, crushing grip that had her completely helpless. His lips came down on hers in a savage kiss that was like nothing she had ever imagined possible. Wordlessly, helplessly, she struggled for a moment, trying to resist a force stronger than anything she had known. There was nothing gentle in his kiss – it was a punishment, savage and brutal. And yet – wildly, irresistibly, she was drawn to respond to that urgent fever of his mouth. Then abruptly he released her, his chest heaving, his voice slightly thick as he ground out: 'And I won't apologize – because if I did I wouldn't mean it.'

Shocked, shaking, she gasped: 'You – you – is that how *you* fight women?'

He looked at her for a moment, lifted his hand and tilted her chin. Light glittered in his eyes. 'If you like – yes.' But the laugh that followed was cynical with no trace of amusement.

'You're vile – loathsome.'

'I know. So you mustn't be surprised when I behave badly.' And he turned and strode away towards the house leaving Jane standing there alone – but not quite alone. Her eye was caught by a movement nearby and she turned to see Colin step out of the shadows He walked towards her.

'Well, well,' he said softly. 'That was a nice little scene.'

She had never seen him like this before, absolutely furious. 'I came out to rescue you from Gavin – seeing that you "don't get on". I can see I needn't have bothered. You were both doing very well.'

'It wasn't what it seemed,' she said unsteadily. 'Really, I—' 'Don't bother,' he cut in. 'I *saw* for myself. Oh, boy, you sure had me fooled. And I thought you were shy!'

'Colin, don't, please.' She was nearly crying now. Everything was going so very wrong. She reached out to touch his arm, but he brushed her away and turning, strode off to the house. Jane closed her eyes. Would this nightmare never end?

CHAPTER NINE

As Jane lay in bed the following morning, reluctant to get up and face the day, her mind went back naggingly to the events of the previous night. With dreadful clarity she saw the scene at the house when she had gone back in. Gavin had been dancing smoochily with Sara, while Colin held Kay in his arms. Megan, dear Megan had seen instantly that something was amiss, and had taken Jane under her wing.

She sat up abruptly. This introspection was no use – it was only making things worse. What she had to do now was get up, get dressed, and spend a quiet day with her father.

'I enjoyed the wedding,' he told her later, as she sat on the patio eating a belated breakfast. 'I hadn't realized how much I'd lost touch with people until I got talking to Arthur Murray. He's asked us over one night next week for supper – and d'you know, I'm looking forward to going!'

Jane smiled fondly at him. 'I'm glad, Father. And you are going to see this friend of Mac's this week, aren't you?'

'Hm, Mac's bullied me into it! I think it's only an excuse for him to have a couple of nights out away from work – but still,' he shrugged, 'I'll go.'

'I'm so happy to hear it.' She looked across the table at him. 'And you really do look so much better than when I first came.' She reached out to touch his hand. 'May I stay here and live with you?' She hadn't meant to say it yet, but something made the words come out, and she was rewarded by the glow of sheer happiness that lit his face.

'Jane! Oh, my dear! You will – you really want to?'

She nodded. 'Yes, really. Truly – if you'll have me!'

He threw back his head in a roar of laughter. 'Ah, wait till I tell Mac! He can keep his specialist friend! Who needs doctors now? You've just given me the best cure any man could have.'

Half laughing, half crying, Jane protested, 'Oh, you must go – oh dear!'

'Don't worry, I'm joking. Of course, now I've promised, but it's quite unnecessary, I know that.' He looked at his watch. 'He'll be here soon. Excuse me, I'll have a word with Ellen.' He shook his head wonderingly, and went into the house.

I've done it now, thought Jane. Committed myself – so I'll just have to learn to live with this pain in my heart. It'll go, in time, and I'll learn to grow an extra skin so that Gavin won't be able to hurt me with his contempt. I've done the right thing, I know, and Father is important, not that man. Not ever Gavin.

She finished her breakfast and went into the house.

On Tuesday Gavin came to the house with Mac at seven-thirty to pick up her father to go to the airport. And Sara was in the car. Sara! She should have known!

Jane stood on the step with Ellen to wave them off, trying not to look at Gavin, who had greeted her distantly, as if reluctant to speak at all. 'Don't forget to phone me tonight,' she called, as her father got into the Mercedes.

'I'll not forget,' he assured her. 'You'll be all right?'

'Of course. Ellen will look after me, won't you, Ellen?'

'I sure will. An' you look after Mr. Ritchie, now,

Doctor, you hear me?' Ellen had tears glinting in her brown eyes as she spoke.

'I promise, Ellen,' Mac assured her solemnly with hand on heart.

And so they went. Jane was left standing on the step as they vanished out of sight, and there was a yawningly empty feeling inside her. She had been here barely two weeks, and already she would miss this tall kindly man, her father, who was going to be away for one night. It was then that she knew she had made the right decision. Whatever happened in the future, she and her father were reunited.

She and Ellen turned and went in, and Ellen put a motherly hand on Jane's shoulder. 'Don't you fret, child. Your dad will be okay, I can feel it in my bones.'

'I think you're right, Ellen. I'm sure he will.' Jane said, but in her mind was Gavin's face as he had looked at her only minutes before, and it wrenched at her heart. A flat, dismissive glance, it had confirmed all her secret unhappiness. Oh, why was he so cruel? And why, oh, why was she such a fool? She hadn't imagined that faint triumphant smile on Sara's face as she had waved goodbye, had she?

She ran upstairs to get ready for Megan's arrival at eight.

It was different working at the school with her instead of with Ann, and Jane managed – not without effort – to put all thoughts of Gavin and Sara at the back of her mind. Megan was full of the wedding, and the reception, and how much John had enjoyed it, and she tactfully avoided all reference to Gavin or Colin, for which Jane was thankful.

Her father phoned that evening, full of good spirits, to

say he had seen the specialist, and had some tests, but that the man wanted him to stay another day or so, if possible. Jane, sensing that her father was more concerned about her well-being than his own, assured him that he must stay as long as necessary. He rang off, reassured, after promising to ring her the following evening.

The next day Jane and Megan spent shopping in Port Patrick, and gossiping over iced coffee at Megan's home. As Jane was about to leave at tea time, guilty at leaving Ellen alone so long, Megan said: 'Colin and I have been asked to some friends in Port Patrick tonight, the Steadmans – I think you met them at the wedding. Would you like to come with us, as your father's away?'

'Thanks, Megan, but I'd better not. Father's ringing again this evening – and there are loads of books that I'm itching to get my hands on – would you believe I haven't had a chance to read since I came?'

Megan laughed. 'All right. But if he rings early, and you change your mind, let me know. We'll be going about seven-thirty.'

'I will, thanks.'

She walked home slowly in the heat, refusing Megan's offer of a lift, feeling, for the first time, very lonely. She let herself into the house and called: 'Ellen, I'm home!'

There was no answer. The house remained silent, with only the faint echo of Jane's words lingering in the still, warm air. Puzzled, Jane went through to the kitchen, expecting to find the housekeeper dozing. Instead there was a note propped up against the tea caddy on the table. Jane picked it up, sensing that something was wrong, and read:

Dear Miss Jane, My brother-in-law phoned to say my sister is ill, and I have gone to look after the kids while he is at work. Will be home on the bus tonight. Sorry but could not let you know. Your dinner is in fridge. Yours Truly, Ellen.'

'Oh, dear!' Jane put the letter down. For a moment she was tempted to ring Megan and tell her, then realized that Colin would soon be home. No, she didn't want to see him – not yet anyway.

There was nothing else for it but to make the best of her enforced solitude, enjoy her leisure, and wait for her father's call, and Ellen's return. She went upstairs and showered, changed into shorts and top, loosened her hair from the ribbon that kept it tidy, and warmed her tea, a delicious concoction of fish and rice.

Afterwards Jane went to sit out on the patio with a long iced lime drink and a pile of her father's paperbacks. It was so quiet and pleasant, with only the occasional gleam of a bird's wing, caught by the sun, to disturb the stillness. The air was heavy with the scent of flowers, and fat bumble-bees droned dazily, replete with rich nectar. A further sound broke the stillness, the noise of a plane, but when that had stopped, all was quiet again. Jane had thought she would feel lonelier now, but strangely, she did not. She picked up the top one of the pile of books, a thriller by Alistair Maclean, and began to read.

She was so engrossed in it that it was a shock to discover, when she was disturbed by an unusual sound, that it had begun to rain. Jane put the book down, watching the huge heavy drops splashing down outside the shelter of the patio. Rain! Somehow she had forgotten that such a thing existed here. She watched, fascinated, as it grew more insistent, and the air changed and became colder, and even the birds were still. She stood and went into the garden, feeling the parched soil beneath her soaking in the much-needed moisture. She lifted her face to feel the cool drops splashing on her cheeks, and she laughed. This was marvellous, quite unlike English rain. The drops were enormous, soft, and oddly soothing. After a few minutes, realizing that she would be completely soaked if she stayed there any longer, she reluctantly went back into the shelter of the patio. And there she stayed, watching, marvelling at the flowers, which seemed to grow brighter and richer before her eyes.

She heard the phone ring and went quickly inside.

'Hello?'

The line crackled distantly, and then her father's voice came, very faint, each word punctuated with static so that she had to strain her ears to hear.

'Jane? Everything's fine. I've seen that doctor fellow again – can you hear me?'

'Just about,' she answered. 'What does he say?' She spoke slowly and loudly.

'He thinks my trouble is nervous in origin—' the line faded and then his voice came back faintly, '—wants me to have a few more tests but doesn't think there's much to worry about—' his voice vanished completely, and Jane said: 'The line's awful, but I'm glad, Father. Can you hear me?'

'Yes, just about. Jane, is everything all right your end?'

She had to strain her ears to hear anything now. 'Yes,' she said. 'Everything's fine.' It was no use trying to explain about Ellen.

'Good. I told Gavin—' the line crackled so loudly that it almost deafened her. She held the receiver away from her ear.

'I can't hear you,' she shouted.

'No, it's terrible, I'll try and ring you later—' again the fade out, followed by: 'All right? 'Bye, Jane.'

' 'Bye, Father. Don't worry.'

She hung up and rubbed her ear in relief. What had he been going to say? It didn't matter; the important thing was plain enough. The specialist clearly thought there was nothing seriously wrong with her father. Perhaps, if he rang later, when the rain had stopped, the line would be normal. But now all she felt was a profound sensation of relief. So they might stay another day or so? She smiled wryly. Gavin would hardly say anything, but he would be itching to get back to work. Do him good! she thought, as she returned slowly to the patio, switching on lights as she went. Night had come even more swiftly than usual, with the rain, and now the lights added an extra dimension to the water falling steadily outside, reflecting it back, a shiny impenetrable wall of silver that shimmered and moved as if it were alive.

Jane stood and watched, fascinated, for a while before carrying the books into the lounge and sitting down again. Ellen would be home soon – if the bus was running in this. If . . . But it was no use wondering. Jane resolutely began to read again.

It was about half an hour later that the quality of the rain changed, and suddenly slowed its headlong pelt down to become quieter. Jane looked up, thinking it was about to stop, when – CRASH! A vivid crackle of lightning lit the entire sky with bright yellow, and the lights jumped and flickered. Almost immediately, and right overhead, came the even louder crash of thunder, a long low, vicious-sounding roll that echoed hollowly round the sky before diminishing. She put her book down and stood up. Her heart beat faster, and although she tried to fight the panic down, it persisted. She had had an irrational fear of storms ever since she had seen a tree split clean in two by lightning, when she was a child. She knew the power, had seen it . . . Quickly she went and pulled the curtains together, and that was a little better, but she found herself waiting for the next flash, and now she was shaking. She looked at her watch. Eight-fifteen, and Megan would have gone, before the storm – and Ellen – where would she be?

Jane put a hand to her face, fighting for calm, feeling more alone and frightened than ever before in her life. And then, distantly, she heard the long, mournful howl of a dog, and her scalp prickled with terror. Then she remembered. Carlo! It was Carlo, and he would be all alone – for the housekeeper would be cosily settled in her house, and not listening to hear a frightened dog, for he was sheltered and safe – or was he? The howl came again, and somehow, in the midst of Jane's own fear, was born a kind of courage. She saw Carlo's face, his trusting brown eyes as they had watched her, and she knew that she had to do something to help him.

He would be company too – even if she had to carry him back – or stay there. But there was no way for her to get in, only a dog-flap in the bottom of the kitchen door. Would he use it when she called? She had to try, she knew that now. There was another, brighter flash, followed by thunder, and Jane ran to the kitchen. There would be something to put over her, somewhere, and it was better to go now, and get it over with – and her own fear diminished slightly in her concern for an animal.

She opened cupboards and drawers feverishly. Brooms and brushes, pots and pans. Ah, yes, that was it! She had known, had seen it before – with a little cry of relief Jane pulled out the large polythene sheet from the bottom drawer of the sink unit, and shook it out. And there was nothing that would deter her now, not even the thought of trying to manage, carrying a dog, and shelter underneath the sheet at the same time. The main thing was to get there, and find him, and then worry about returning.

She waited by the back door, calmer now, waiting for the next flash so that she could run immediately out, for there was an interval of time in between, and – there it was, and she flinched, but opened the door quickly, pulled the sheet of plastic over her head, and ran out towards Gavin's house.

Jane slipped and slithered along the path from the back door towards the thick trees that separated the two houses in a kind of no-man's-land that was dark and terrifying, but a merciful short cut. She was under them now, a doubtful shelter in a storm, and the sooner out the better. Then she stopped her headlong run. Stopped because of what she was seeing – but not really believing – until that dark shape that wasn't a tree moved and came towards her. Jane screamed in a frenzy of terror, hearing the sound as if from a great distance as yet another, nearer flash lit the shape, and it became a man, a man who was coming at her with hands upraised. Then she heard her name called: 'Jane!' and the world and rain and the night all mingled in a dizzy spiral as she fell against him in a dead faint.

Jane opened her eyes and saw Gavin standing beside her. Panic, that had nothing at all to do with the storm, filled her and she sat up quickly on the big settee, and looked around her, feeling her clothes clinging soddenly to her body. She was in a room she had not seen before, a large, well furnished room, quietly luxurious – and safe from whatever was outside.

He spoke. 'We're in my home, Jane.'

'Oh.' She digested that small piece of information, and saw Carlo sitting beside her, his face anxious, as if he knew …

'Carlo,' she whispered, and put out a hand. She couldn't think yet.

'What were you doing?' Gavin asked, and she looked up at him properly, seeing his hair, shiny with rain, his wet shirt and jacket clinging to him, and something made her answer: 'I was coming h-here to make sure Carlo was safe – I heard him howling – w-where were you – oh!' she started as lightning flashed close outside the window, and with a little 'pop', all the lights went out. There was a thunderous crash, seemingly from the ceiling, and she jumped to her feet, to find Gavin's arm steadying her.

'It's all right,' he said soothingly. 'I'll get a torch—'

She struggled free. 'I'm not s-stopping h-here,' she stammered, 'not with *you*.'

'Don't be a little fool,' he grated, his voice low and harsh. 'You're safe here – and you're stopping while this is on, at least.'

The room was completely in darkness. She couldn't see either Gavin or Carlo, only a vast, tingling blackness that was overwhelming. Blindly turning, she fell against the settee, and heard a muffled oath as he touched her arm and said: 'For heaven's sake stop trying to get away. I can't even—' and he held her tighter as she tried to push him away. 'It's no use, I'm not letting you move. Just stop panicking for a moment and listen to me.'

With an abrupt, completely unexpected movement, he pulled her down beside him on the settee, and she felt Carlo jump up on her knee and begin to lick her wet face.

'Jane, what's the matter? Why were you coming here?'

'To see if Carlo was all right. I didn't know *you* were here,' she said weakly.

'You came out alone, in *that*, for a *dog*!' His voice was

185

eloquent. His arms were around her now, and to her horror Jane realized that she had stopped struggling.

'I heard him howl,' she managed more calmly. 'I thought he was terrified – he *sounded* it. I didn't expect to b-bump into you.'

'I was coming over to make sure you and Ellen were safe. He hates me leaving him in thunder.'

'Ellen's gone to her sister's. I was alone.' She began to shiver helplessly with delayed shock.

'You poor kid!' There was none of the usual scorn she had come to expect in his voice. Nothing, except perhaps pity, and she didn't need that. She stirred uneasily, suddenly aware that those arms weren't moving away, were in fact tightening.

'There's no need to feel sorry for me,' she managed, wincing as a jagged streak of yellow lit the room. 'Please—'

'You're scared stiff. Don't be, Jane. You're with me.'

'Yes, I know *that*.' Bitterness filled her voice. 'But I don't need *you* – ever.'

Thunder shook the room, an ornament moved and fell somewhere near them, and Jane trembled. But it was no longer with fear of the storm. It was because of Gavin's disturbing nearness.

In the silence that followed the cessation of noise, she heard his breathing, and sensed his hand near her face, and she felt stifled.

'Don't – don't—' she whispered. Then she felt his lips on hers. And this was no savage kiss, but gentle, and warm, filling her with treacherous weakness. When it was over, she whispered in a voice that shook: 'Why are you so cruel? You hate me!'

'Oh, Jane, if only you knew!' he said softly, a tremor in his voice. 'If only you knew. I can't—' he stopped, and

tightened his arms round her. 'Don't stop me. Don't—'
and then his mouth was on hers again. It was the kiss of a
man who knows that he mustn't, at any cost, be less than
tender, and she felt herself responding to that tingling
warmth. Helplessly, shamelessly, she clung to him, and
when at last he pulled himself reluctantly away, it was to
say: 'It's no use, Jane. I can't fight it – or you – any more.
Say you don't hate me.'

'H-hate you?' a sob escaped. If only he knew!

He touched her chin gently, found her cheek and
stroked it, there in the dark, and he whispered: 'All right,
I don't deserve anything from you – but for what it's
worth, I love you. Now go ahead, laugh.'

Her heart threatened to burst. 'Wha – say that again,'
she said, disbelieving her ears.

'I – love – you. I've never said it to any woman before –
I never intended to tell you – but I can't help myself.' He
groaned. 'Why aren't you laughing? Don't you find it
hilarious?'

'No,' she said softly. 'I just don't believe it, that's all. Is
it s-some kind of a j-joke? I don't think it's funny at all,'
and a sob broke through.

'Oh, my Jane, my darling. Stop it. Don't cry – please
don't cry. I can't bear to hear you crying.'

'You're not joking!' It was said in a tone of dawning
wonder. Even the storm was forgotten. That no longer
troubled her. She reached out and touched his face. 'Say
it again,' she asked softly.

'I love you.' The simple, age-old words rang true, she
knew that now.

'And I love you. But I thought you hated me.'

'I wanted to. I've been fighting this ever since that first
time we met. Then you remember how I came in when
you'd been playing the guitar?' She nodded, the memory

coming back clearly. 'I saw you then, and it was like nothing that had ever happened to me before. You sat on the floor, intent on your music, your hair falling over your face, your sweet face,' he cupped it gently, 'and I knew what was happening to me – and I was frightened. You were – are – so young. I'm thirty-one – thirteen years older than you. I kept trying to remind myself that you were a little schemer who—' at her exclamation of pain he put his finger to her lips. 'No, my love, hear me out – I must say it. All right, of course I know you're not. But I had to have something to cling to, to keep my sanity. Everything you did, or said, was beautiful to me, and I was terrified, because you're so young, only a girl. That night after Sara's party—' she stiffened instinctively at the memory of humiliation. 'Please, Jane, let me tell you. I wanted you so very much – I had to tell myself to control this urge. That was why I—' he stopped.

'I understand now,' she murmured.

'But not only that – *you* seemed to dislike me so. It put me on my mettle. Who the hell were *you*, I told myself, to get under my skin like that?' He reached out his other hand and gently smoothed her forehead. 'I suppose I set up an automatic defence mechanism – and so appeared, to you, more arrogant than ever – but it was only to stop me grabbing hold of you and making love to you.' He laughed softly. 'It nearly let me down that day in the store, you remember, when you came to see the material? My God! I nearly forgot everything then—'

'And I thought I'd done something to make you angry,' she murmured.

'Oh, you had! But not in the way you thought! I've been a fool, Jane. Will you ever forgive me?'

'I'll have to try,' she said, but her heart was singing. 'I realized that I loved you in church, at the wedding. I was watching you, and suddenly I knew, just like that. I'd been fighting it too, in a different way, because – because—' she stopped.

'Go on,' he prompted. 'I can take anything *now*.'

'Because I thought you were in love with Sara, and everyone said—'

He groaned. 'I know. You don't have to tell me. I've known Sara for years, and Kay too. But I don't love either of them. Never have – I've never loved anyone until now, until you came into my life. I know I'm not a very nice person – I'm selfish, I've had most of my own way in everything until now.' He paused, and went on more thoughtfully: 'But you've opened my eyes. You've made me see that money, and work, aren't everything. You've changed my life, as well as your father's. Jane, will you stay here, on Saramanca, and marry me?'

'Oh yes,' she answered. 'Oh yes, Gavin.'

The storm was dying away outside. The lightning was further away, the thunder fainter. It had served its purpose, thought Jane, as she lay in the warmth of Gavin's arms. It had brought them both to their senses.